"Tell Us Some

A Third Assembly Book

A Further 108 Stories
for Primary School
Worship Assemblies,

with Prayers, suggested Hymns,
and Teachers' Notes,
for Autumn, Spring,
and Summer Terms.

(This book may be used in conjunction
with the first volume, "Tell us a Story,"
and with the second volume, "Tell us Another".)

Rev. Dr. George E. Stewart,
B.A., M.A.

Published by
Topical Resources

© **Rev. Dr. George E. Stewart, B.A., M.A.**

First Published May 1998

Published by:
Topical Resources

P.O. Box 329,
Broughton,
Preston,
PR3 5LT

For latest catalogue: Tel: 01772 863158

ISBN 1 872977 32 4

Typeset and Printed by T. Snape & Co. Ltd., Boltons Court, Preston, Lancashire.
Tel: 01772 254553

Preface

"Tell Us Some More" is a Third volume of stories written for the Worship Assembly of the Primary School. The required fifth re-printing of the first volume. and the reprinting of the second volume, revealed the keen interest taken by Headteachers and Religious Experts in what happens in the Primary School Assembly.

Both County schools, and Church schools, of all the major denominations have found the first and second books useful. The stories, prayers, and suggested hymns are intended to be an aid for busy Primary Teachers.

The simple, fast moving style, and the language of the stories had been chosen deliberately. The stories are meant to be told, rather than read. The style of story-telling has been adapted to suit the wide age range of Primary School pupils. Qualified Teachers have constructively criticised them, and the style and language has been amended where it was thought to be necessary.

The stories cover the three terms of a school year. Each week has a single theme, dealt with by two stories applicable to the children's life experience, and one story from the Bible. A short prayer is added after each story, based on the theme for the week. A hymn is suggested, taken from one of three popular Hymn Books used by Primary Schools.

A "Teachers' Note" has been added at the end of each story, which usually makes three valid points. Biblical References have been added. The story as it unfolds, usually contains a moral, or a social problem, which is of interest to the children. They are meant to be involved in the moral decisions, as the Teacher tells the story.

I have been influenced in my writing by the answers which I received to a Questionaire which I sent out to thirty Primary schools. The Headteachers' reply listed the difficulties of the Worship Assembly, as: (1) The Pupil's limited attention span. (2) The Pupils live in a television age, and consequently, pictures come easier to children than words. (3) Worship is not always pitched at the child's age level. (4) Religion is not relevant to the parental background. (5) Pupils, generally, no longer attend Sunday School.

Although the book is based on the progression of the school year, the stories may be used individually to suit events in the school, or in the pupil's life experience, eg. an accident, a local celebration, a birthday, Christian Aid Week, a farewell, holidays, or the recognised special days. The choice is left to the professionalism, integrity, and sensitivity of the Teacher.

The stories have been written under the provisions of the 1988 Education Reform Act, where a distinction has been drawn between the Worship Assembly, and Religious Education. The book has been written with, "a broadly Christian approach." It treats the stories objectively, without denominational bias. It leaves the matter of interpretation to the Teacher, and to the imagination of the children.

There are many stories here which could readily be used by Sunday School Teachers, or in Church Family Services.

Contents

Autumn Term

Week 1
Theme: *Caring for the Environment*

(a)   Litter-Bugs 2

(b)   Children of the Rain-forests 3

(c)   Cain and Abel............................5

Week 2
Theme: *Social Needs*

(a)   The Drop-Outs 7

(b)   The Travelling People 9

(c)   The Man at the Pool 12

Week 3
Theme: *Harvest*

(a)   Lettuces 14

(b)   Three laws of Harvest 15

(c)   Weeds among the Wheat..........17

Week 4
Theme: *The Future*

(a)   The Lonely Duckling 19

(b)   Surprise Roses..........................21

(c)   The Disappointing Vineyard 22

Week 5
Theme: *Duty*

(a)   Falling Asleep 24

(b)   The Little Dutch Hero 25

(c)   Mary, Mother of Jesus 27

Week 6
Theme: *Jealousy*

(a)   The Organist and Artist............30

(b)   The Birthday Card....................31

(c)   Jacob and Esau 33

Week 7
Theme: *The Sikhs*

(a)   Guru Nanak 36

(b)   The Five "Ks" 37

(c)   The Khalsa 39

Week 8
Theme: *Usefulness*

(a)   Edinburgh Time 40

(b)   Charlie's Walking Stick 42

(c)   Paying Taxes 44

Week 9
Theme: *Theme*

(a)   R. L. Stevenson's Epitaph........46

(b)   A Friend in Need......................48

(c)   Simon the Helper 50

Week 10
Theme: *Poetry*

(a)   Abou Ben Adhem's Dream......52

(b)   Caedmon Singer and Poet........53

(c)   The Shortest Psalm...................55

Week 11
Theme: *Towards Christmas*

(a)   Snowball the Rabbit 57

(b)   The Little Pup..........................59

(c)   The Wise Men 60

Week 12
Theme: *Christmas*

(a)   Tammy's Hair 62

(b)   A Christmas Carol....................64

(c)   Christmas Questions 66

Spring Term

Week 1
Theme: *New Beginnings*

(a)   Martha Thompson's Hymn 70

(b)   St. Augustine of Hippo.............72

(c)   Fall from a Window 73

Week 2
Theme: *Fear*

(a)   The Haunted House..................75

(b)   The Imaginative Friend............77

(c)   I was Afraid.............................79

Week 3
Theme: *More Social Needs*

(a)   Mother Teresa 81

(b)   The Bagpipes............................82

(c)   The Great Catch of Fish...........85

Week 4
Theme: *On Trust*

(a)   A Fishy Story 86

(b)   Polycarp 88

(c)   Jesus in the Synagogue 89

Week 5
Theme: *Birds*

(a)   Robin Readbreast 92

(b)   The Leprechaun........................94

(c)   The Bramble King....................95

Week 6
Theme: *Danger*

(a)   The Igloo 96

(b)   Look before you Leap..............98

(c)   Poisonous Snakes...................100

Week 7
Theme: *The Church Family*

(a)   The Red Hot Coal 102

(b)   The Princess Victoria.............104

(c)   The Epileptic Boy 106

Week 8
Theme: *Muslims*

(a)   The Muslim Boy 108

(b)   More about the Muslim Boy ..109

(c)   Ali's Sermon 110

Week 9
Theme: *Lost and Found*

(a)   St. Patrick's Day 112

(b)   Robin finds a Friend..............114

(c)   The Older Brother 115

Week 10
Theme: *Dependable People*

(a)   The Stand-in 117

(b)   Helping Hands........................119

(c)   Moses the Prince 120

Week 11
Theme: *Hospitals*

(a)   Albert Schweitzer...................122

(b)   Good Friends..........................124

(c)   The Good Samaritan 126

Week 12
Theme: *Towards Easter*

(a)   The Towel 128

(b)   The Cross 129

(c)   The Egg 131

Summer Term

Week 1
Theme: *Fools*

(a)   April Fool 134

(b)   A Wise Fool 135

(c)   People like Animals 137

Week 2
Theme: *Leadership*

(a)   David is Anointed King 139

(b)   The May Queen......................140

(c)   Peter's Mobile Phone 142

Week 3
Theme: *Children*

(a)   The New Baby 144

(b)   The Japanese Jug...................146

(c)   Ben's Lunch 149

Week 4
Theme: *Mothers*

(a)   Mother Susanna......................150

(b)   Mother Cat 153

(c)   Jesus and the Children...........154

Week 5
Theme: *Friendship*

(a)   Greyfriar's Bobby 156

(b)   Two Good Friends 158

(c)   A Friend at Mid-Night 159

Week 6
Theme: *Welfare*

(a)   The School Nurse...................161

(b)   Rebecca's Engagement 163

(c)   David's Kindness 164

Week 7
Theme: *Mystery*

(a)   Coin in Fish's Mouth 166

(b)   Mystery of Evil 168

(c)   The Oil Mystery 169

Week 8
Theme: *Trying One's Best*

(a)   The Flower Show 171

(b)   The Car Thief.........................173

(c)   Mary and Martha....................175

Week 9
Theme: *The Jews*

(a)   Abraham the Father................176

(b)   Praying for Others.................178

(c)   Isaiah's Call...........................179

Week 10
Theme: *Second things*

(a)   Second Sight 181

(b)   Second Wind..........................182

(c)   Second Hand Books 184

Week 11
Theme: *Small Things*

(a)   For the Want of a Nail...........187

(b)   Lost Needle in a Hay-Barn.....188

(c)   Little Accidents 190

Week 12
Theme: *Sayings of Jesus*

(a)   Salt of the Earth.....................192

(b)   Narcissus and Jesus................194

(c)   The Two Fears 196

Hymn Book Abbreviations.

The suggested Hymns for these Worship Assemblies are to be found in one of three popular Hymn Books used by Schools.

(C. & P.1.) Come and Praise. Book 1.   B.B.C. Publications

(C. & P.2.) Come and Praise Book 2.   B.B.C. Publications

(J. P.) Junior Praise. (Combined Words Edition.)

Marshall Pickering

Autumn Term

2

Many years ago, there was a school which used to hold a "Paper-chase" at the end of every school term. As the term passed by, the pupils used to collect old newspapers. They cut them up into small pieces. These small pieces of paper were stored in old jute sugar sacks.

On the last day of term, two or three boys would take the sacks of paper cuttings, and run off. They ran in a circle of about three miles. As they ran, they pulled out handfuls of paper, letting it fall behind them. The runners left a trail of paper over the meadow, between the trees, and across the hedges, and down farm tracks. Of course, the sacks became lighter in weight, the further they ran.

About twenty minutes later, all the remaining children would rush out of the school gates. The paper chase was on. Those running behind would follow the trail of paper across the countryside. They ran as fast as they could, in order to try to catch the first runners. Sometimes, one of the first runners would leave a second false trail of paper going in the wrong direction to confuse those running behind.

It was all very good fun. Usually the first runners were able to get back to the school before they were caught. In the paper chase, the children who followed had to run across streams, and through farmyards, and even through the church yard, looking for the trail of paper. In a few hours, everyone was safe back at school again. The paper chase had finished.

Now, the sad thing was that no-one ever went out to pick up the paper again. No-one seemed to realise that the farmer's cows and bullocks would eat the paper which was lying on the grass. The cows became sick. The sheep and their lambs also ate the paper.

When the rain fell, the paper became wet and soggy. The grassy meadows looked dirty with so much wet paper lying about. The wind blew the paper into the little rivers that flowed through the meadows. The school never realised that they were harming their environment. The children went home at the end of the term, very happy indeed.

When the new term began, the children all came back to school. A new lady teacher, Mrs. Keen, who was very concerned about the environment, also arrived. When she heard about the paper chase, she went out into the woods, to see what damage had been done. She saw the messy wet paper lying about everywhere. Going back to the school, Mrs. Keen held an assembly and explained to the children, that the environment was a gift from God to people. Just as a family had to learn to keep their home and bedrooms tidy, so also we must learn to keep our countryside tidy. The school-governors were also so much concerned that they decided never to have another paper chase again.

The farmer was pleased when he heard the good news. The church verger was pleased, when he heard that he would never again have to get down on his hands and knees to collect the paper lying among the grave-stones. The lambs no longer choked on the paper, as they were eating the green grass. The cows did not become sick, by swallowing paper when they drank from the river.

At the end of the term, Mrs. Keen taught the children a new game. She named the game, "Cops and Robbers." Half the number of children, boys and girls, tied a piece of wool around their arms. They were the "robbers". The other half had no wool around their arms. They were the "cops". The cops had to chase the robbers, catch them, and break the wool around their arms. Remembering about keeping the environment clean, the cops had to put the broken wool into their pockets, to show just how many robbers they had caught. Everyone whose woollen armband was broken became a member of the 'cops' team. The children had a wonderful game, but this time, it did not harm the environment.

Nowadays, there are many plastic bags lying about the countryside. If a farm animal should eat one, it could die. Old broken fishing lines along a river bank, can entangle round a swan's feet. Broken bottles lying about often cut dogs' and cats' paws. Let us promise to keep our school clean and tidy. Bits of paper must be put into the rubbish bin. Do not allow yourself to become a litter-bug!

Prayer:

> Lord, we thank you for the countryside.
> We thank you for the beauty of the world.
> Teach us to keep our environment tidy.
> When on holiday, help us keep the beaches clean.
> Let us not throw paper about our school.   Amen.

Hymn:

> All things bright and beautiful. (C&P.1. 3) (JP. 6)

Teacher's Note: (1) The meaning of this story will be obvious to the children without much comment. (Keeping our environment clean). (2) Ask the children, "How do we get rid of plastic waste". (3). The religious message is that this world is both God's world, and our world.

(b) Children of the Rain Forests   *Week 1.   Caring for the Environment*

Paulino, and Marco, were native boys. Marie and Sara were native girls. They belonged to the Kaiapo people, who live in the rain forests of Brazil. The children were very poor. They belonged to one of the small villages alongside the Amazon river.

The four children had heard that men from the cities were coming with tractors and machinery to cut down the trees in their forest. The trees of the rain forest were very high. These trees had taken about two hundred years to grow. Usually, they were hardwood trees, such as mahogany or teak. The hardwoods were were used in Europe and in the United States to make furniture.

The wood-cutters arrived and set up a logging camp. They came with their tractors and machine-saws, to cut down the best of the trees. At first, the four children found it exciting to watch the men cutting down these high trees. First, the wood-cutters used chain-saws to fell the trees to the ground. Then they lopped off the tree branches. They collected the branches and left them in large piles. Then, they used their powerful tractors to drag away the tree trunks to the newly built saw-mills. The trees would later be sawn up into planks of hardwood, dried, and shipped overseas.

Next, the woodmen made huge bonfires of the heaps of branches. The smoke made the children's eyes smart. All this cutting and burning, made the forest appear to be an untidy mess. The woodmen set fire to the large patch of the forest, which they had partly cleared. A wide area began to burn, and that really frightened the rain-forest children. They watched the wild animals, and snakes and birds, and frogs, and squirrels, all trying to escape from the approaching fire. The children also had to run to get out of the way. The four children ran back into the damp rain forest to tell their parents what was happening.

After few days, the area had been burned down to the ground. Later, the woodmen, came back with tractors dragging ploughs behind them. They ploughed up the top-soil, and sowed grass seed everywhere. Soon the ground would change into grass-lands, and farmers and cattle-ranchers would move in to the area. Cows and sheep in hundreds would feed on the new grass fields.

The village Headman called the native people together. He had attended the mission school when he had been a boy. He had learned many things, that the villagers did not yet understand. The Headman said to his people. "What these woodmen are doing to the rain forest is bad for our people. Did you not see the animals running away from the flames? This will happen to us. Soon, we too will be forced to move away, deeper into the forest." The four children began to understand what was happening.

The Headman said, "The rain forests are like great sponges, they soak up the water. The moisture coming out of the leaves goes into the air and forms clouds. The clouds pour down life-giving rain. If anyone takes the trees away, then the land will dry up. Trees breath in carbon dioxide, and they breathe out oxygen. To live, people need to breathe in oxygen."

The village Headman continued to explain to the people. He said, "If we allow trees to remain, tree leaves will continue to breath out oxygen. This will make more oxygen for people and animals on the earth to breathe in."

He said, "These woodcutters do not really need to cut down all our trees, anyway. The furniture manufacturers could easily use soft woods such as Pine Trees. Pines only take thirty years to grow. These hardwood trees have taken at least two hundred years to grow. We must preserve them." Paulino, Marco, Marie, and Sara were inclined to agree with the Village headman. The children joined their parents in the protest march around the wood-cutters camp. Sadly, no-one in authority took any notice of their protests.

Sure enough, the native forest people had to move away, just like the animals. Other people, mostly new farmers, moved in to the fresh grass land. Cattle began to graze on the farms. The rain-forest children, Paulino, Marco, Marie, and Sara, had to find a new home deeper in the forest. Wood from the trees was exported by ships to America and Europe.

What will the natives do, when the woodmen again catch up with their new settlement? Will this taking of the land ever stop? Do you think this was fair? Did you know that Britain was once covered by a great forest?

Prayer:

> Heavenly Father, you have given us a wonderful world.
> We thank you for the rain forests which remain.
> Teach people to understand and value them.
> Bless the children of the rain forests.
> Bless the children of our school.   Amen.

Hymn:

> You shall go out with joy, and be led forth with peace. (C&P.2. 98)
> (Sung slowly at first, and the second time faster.)

Teachers' Note: (1) This story teaches that our environment is balanced. Trees, and people bear a relationship to each other. (2) God wants us to manage the environment wisely and kindly. (3) Too much carbon dioxide in the air causes "Global Warming".

(c) Cain and Abel   *Week 1.   Caring for the Environment*

There are many ways of managing the environment. The Bible tells us a story about Adam and Eve's two sons. Cain was the elder son, and Abel was the younger son. Abel grew up to become a shepherd. In the Near Eastern countries at that time, shepherds lived the life of nomads. This meant that they had to move about from place to place, because there was not much grass to eat, for their flocks of sheep and goats.

When the flock nibbled the grass very short, the shepherd had to lead his sheep to another feeding ground, perhaps, miles away. If the rains fell, and made the grass grow, then the shepherd could always bring his flocks back again, later in the year. Abel's life as a shepherd was a travelling one. He slept in a tent. A fire was kept burning all through the night to frighten away any wolves, which might have attempted to attack the sheep in the darkness.

Cain the elder son, became a "tiller of the ground" which is an old fashioned way of describing a farmer. Because Cain was a farmer, he could not move far away from his fields. He had to live in a farm-house close to his fields. He grew his wheat, potatoes, carrots, and any other vegetables the fields would produce.

One day, Able offered a firstborn lamb from his flock as a sacrifice to God. This meant that the lamb was killed, offered to God, and then eaten afterwards at a meal. Cain also offered a sacrifice unto God, from the fruits on his farm. (It may be that our own judgement of what someone else has performed, may make us compare our efforts with theirs. We may feel that we have not done so well and that may make us jealous of the other person).

No-one really knows just why Cain was so jealous of Abel. Jealousy is always a foolish thing, because each one of us has valuable personal talents. It always honours God when we are doing our best.

Cain thought that God had been pleased with Abel's sacrifice of a lamb, but he also believed that God had rejected his own offering of the fruit of the ground. Cain became very angry. God spoke to Cain in his mind, and asked him why he was so displeased. God made a promise to Cain, "If you do what is right, I will accept you."

Cain became even more jealous of his brother. One day Cain invited Abel to go for a walk in the field with him. Cain waited for the opportune moment, and then he attacked his brother Abel, and killed him. Later that day, The Lord spoke to Cain. He asked "Where is your brother Abel?" Cain replied, "Am I my brother's keeper?" (He meant that he was not responsible for his brother's safety.)

The Lord said to Cain, "Your brother's blood cries out to me from the field. You are under a curse. When you work the ground, it will no longer produce crops for you. You will become a restless wanderer on the earth." Cain cried out, "Lord, my punishment is greater than I can bear. I have been banished from my home. People will want to kill me." The Lord put a mark on Cain, so that no-one would kill him. Cain went out, and lived in the land of Nod.

This story has had many explanations. Many scholars explain the story as if it were a parable, meaning that there was a quarrel in the Jewish nation, between those who wanted to live the pastoral moving life of the shepherd, and those who wanted to remain permanently at home in built -up communities, such as peasant farmers, and villagers.

The shepherd life is like that of Abel, one of travelling about. The Farmer life is like that of Cain, who preferred to settle down, and build farm-houses, make fields, vineyards, and even villages. Have you noticed how we use our environment. In hill country we raise sheep. In country near a river, we build farms, and towns.

The other point is that Cain should not have killed his brother. That was a very wicked thing to do. Families are important. Brothers and sisters should always be loyal to each other. Cain held a grudge against Abel. We should never hold a grudge.

Prayer:

> Good Lord, help us to value our families.
> We thank you for brothers and sisters:
> for cousins, and school friends.
> If we quarrel, teach us to to forgive.
> We pray for shepherd hill- farmers,
> and for settled arable farmers.
> Teach us to share our environment.   Amen.

Hymn:

> I belong to a family, the biggest on earth. (C&P.1. 69)

Teachers' note: (1) Abel and Cain both were good workers in their environment. God loved them both. (2) Jealousy is a very wrong attitude. Often, to just talk together about any quarrel may solve the problem. (3) The commandment says, "Thou shalt not kill". (Reference: Genesis Chap 4.)

(a) The Drop-Outs   *Week 2   Social Needs*

Today, we are going to have hear about the work of a Nineteenth Century Christian Social Mission, known as the Salvation Army, which tackles modern social problems.

Old Sammy was a drop-out. A long time ago, he had a job. He was a storeman in a large factory. Sammy was a good worker. He was fairly paid for his hard work. Sammy began to drink large quantities of alcoholic drinks. At first, he did not spend much money on his drink. Sometimes his job became rather boring, so he began to bring a bottle of whiskey into his work-place.

After a time, Sammy used to slip out of the factory to buy more whiskey. Then Sammy reached that state of where he could not do without his drinks every day.

He smoked as well, so Sammy was spending most of his wages on himself, instead of bringing it home to his wife and family. People used to say that Sammy had a "drink problem."

Sammy began to steal tools out of his store to sell illegally to people outside the factory, in order to get money to buy whiskey. The factory Manager found out, what was happening. Sammy was sacked from his job. What could Sammy do now to earn money? He decided to go to London to find work. He found several jobs in London, but each time the Factory Manager found out that Sammy became undependable, because of his drink problem, then Sammy was always dismissed from his job. Sammy could not hold down even a simple job.

Sammy lived in a Men's Hostel for a while. However, because he was always drunk, Sammy was barred from going into the Hostel. Sammy used to get an old blanket, wrap it round himself, and sleep in a shop doorway. The police used to move Sammy on. When it was dark Sammy found a bench in the public park, and he used to stretch himself out, and go to sleep there. As the bitter winter weather approached, Sammy found that, it became too cold to sleep outside. His chest was sore, and he knew that he was very ill. He gasped for breath on many nights.

One dark night, Sammy was walking in despair through the London streets, when he heard a Salvation Army Band playing a bright happy hymn. Sammy loved the music, so he stood in the cold, listening to the Officers inviting people to become Christians, and to begin a new way of life. Sammy did not do anything that evening. He went to sleep under a bridge near the Thames Embankment. That dark cold night, about eleven o'clock, a Salvation Army Tea Van drew up, and the Officers were giving paper cups of tea, and packets of sandwiches to the drop-out people, who were sleeping inside old cardboard boxes under the bridge.

The Officer this time was a man with a Scottish accent. "He said to Sammy, "I think that you are a slave to alcohol. I am sure that if you prayed, God could heal you. Your craving for drink is really an illness. You would also need to try hard yourself, but Christian friends would help you, to get rid of your bad habit." Sammy thought over what the Salvation army Officer had said. In the darkness, under the bridge, Sammy prayed, "Lord help me to help myself !" Sammy did not feel any different. Yet, he set his mind never to drink again.

When he began to feel better, Sammy went home, to his wife and children again. A kind Christian person provided the money for his train ticket. His family welcomed him home. He felt better in his health after a few weeks. Sammy felt that he had been cured. He felt that God was helping him to leave the drop-out way of life forever. Sammy became a good husband to his wife, and a good father to his children. The Manager gave Sammy his job back, as a factory storeman. Sammy was very thankful for the good work done by the Salvation Army among drop-out people. Eventually, he became a Christian and joined his local Salvation Army Corps.

He could not play a brass musical instrument, so Sammy was allowed to carry the red, gold and blue Salvation Army flag instead. He knew that many other people could drink alcoholic drinks, and still remain good decent people. Sammy knew that he just could not! He had to do without alcohol for the rest of his life. So Sammy signed the pledge, that he would never drink again, and gave up his bad habit forever. Sammy always remembered that God loves all people, including poor people, and drop-out people.

Prayer:

> Heavenly Father, who cares for everyone,
> We thank you for all Christian social workers,
> such as the Salvation Army officers.
> We thank you for the kind people
> who care for needy children.
> Bless and reward those Social Workers,
> who work with the drop-out people.   Amen.

Hymn:

> Colours of day dawn into the mind. (C&P.1. 55) (JP. 28)

Teachers' Note: (1) This lesson may be enlarged to include any Christian Social organisation which cares for "drop-out people" especially those organisations in which you are personally interested. (2) Children may be introduced to the idea that "drop-outs" need skilled treatment because they may be very sick. (In mind). (3) The Biblical "Outcast and beggar" existed in the time of Jesus. Illustrate. this from the New Testament. (St. Luke Chapter 21 verses 1-3. Also Luke Chapter 14 verses 12-14.

(b) The Travelling People

Week 2   Social Needs

Our story today is told to let us think about the way which we look at other people, who may be different in some way to ourselves. These people may be handicapped people, or foreigners, or of a different age group.

The children at Highfield school were rather surprised by three new children, who arrived accompanied by their mother. The children wanted to come to school, while they were in the area. The last school they had attended was about one hundred miles away. Soon, the three childrens' names were written in the school registers. Their mother went away home. The children's names were Sean,

Kathleen, and Dennis O'Malley. When they were asked for their address, the children answered, "O'Malley's Caravan, Station Yard."

The school children became very interested, because the newcomers were very quick to answer any questions. They said that they originally had come from County Mayo, in Eire. The school children asked them if they were Gypsies. "No we are not Gypsies, we are travelling people." Sean answered.

The travelling children spoke with a beautiful Irish accent, in a sing-song, very clear, kind of voice. "Why do you live in a caravan?" the school children asked. "For the same reasons that you live in a house," they replied. "Where do you keep your horse?" the school children asked them. The travelling children winked at each other, and Kathleen said, "We keep the horse below the bed!"

The school children were amazed. On the way home, the three travelling children said to the school children, "If you want to see our horse, then come down to Station Yard, and we will show you where we live." Four of the school children decided to accept the invitation.

Sabrina, Sally, Sam, and Stewart, went down to Station Yard. To their astonishment, there were no old horse-drawn caravans to be seen. Instead, there were four-wheel-drive trucks, and some very modern caravans. Each caravan had a dog kennel outside it, with several big dogs chained up on guard.

The travelling children invited the school children inside to see their home. It was just like a holiday caravan, only larger. It had a fireplace in the living room, with a television, and a bathroom, and several bedrooms. The travelling children's mother welcomed them, and gave them tea and home-made biscuits. She was just like any other children's mother. She made Sean, Kathleen, and Dennis change into their older shoes, and wash their hands.

What does your Dad do? Sally asked Dennis.

"He works, just like anyone else. He can sharpen knives, scissors, or repair grass mowing machines. He is a gardener. a motor mechanic, a window cleaner, a metal worker, and sometimes he collects rags and scrap, or sells cars." Sally was astounded at all this new knowledge about travelling people. Kathleen said, "We will be here about six weeks, because Dad works for the same farmer every year, at the lambing season. In fact, there is nothing my Dad cannot do!"

Kathleen said to the school children, with a big smile, "Actually we have two horses in this caravan. We have the clothes' horse, that Mum uses to put her washing on. That is our first horse. Then, I do not hug a teddy bear, when I go to sleep, I take out my little Woolly Pony, which I hide below the bed during the day. Kathleen reached into the locker below below her bed, and she pulled out a little fluffy horse. The school children laughed loudly.

The children went home to tell their parents about the travelling children. As they were going away, the Doctor was calling on the O'Malleys to register the

O'Malley family at his surgery. Another car drove into the yard. It was the Catholic Priest. He was visiting to welcome the O'Malley family to church, since they were now his Parishioners.

Next day at school, the school children could see that in some subjects, the three travelling children were a little behind the others, because their education was continually being interrupted. Yet, on the other hand, they were very quick learners. They told the Headteacher at Assembly time, that Abraham, Isaac, and Jacob, in Bible times, were all travelling people. They did not live in houses, nor in caravans, but in tents. (Which was true!).

The Teacher tested the travelling children in arithmetic. She asked them if they knew anything about speed. Sean replied that if the speed of your own truck was thirty miles an hour, and it hit a car moving towards you, and it was also travelling at 30 miles an hour, then the speed of crash (impact), must be 60 miles per hour. Sean explained that 30+30 miles per hour added up to 60 miles per hour. Teacher thought a little bit about that, then she said that Sean was correct.

When Kathleen was asked how many feet or metres high a pony might be, she answered by saying, "Please Miss. A good big pony might be about fourteen hands high." The school children had never heard of using "hands" as a measurement.

When Dennis was asked what time it was, he answered without looking at the clock, "It is half past cheese by the village pump." Everyone laughed at that remark. Dennis stood up and apologised, and said that he had not meant to be rude to the Teacher. When she asked him again, what time it was, Dennis answered, "Please Miss, it is time I had my dinner." Again, everyone laughed at the joke!

Their Teacher was a highly trained person, and suddenly, she realised that little Dennis was joking, not to be rude, but to hide the fact from the other children, that he could not tell the time. That week the Teacher bought Dennis a cheap watch, and unknown to anyone, she taught him how to tell the time. The children were finding out in a new way, that while we learn from classes, teachers, and books, yet we also learn from others. They had learnt such a lot about other people and about different ways of life from the travelling children.

About six weeks passed, when Sean, Kathleen, and Dennis came to school, and announced that their Father was moving on to Cornwall. He would be painting up the seaside bathing huts, before the coming of the Summer season. The O'Malleys left school in the middle of the morning at play time. The school children waved goodbye to the three travelling children, as their four-wheel-drive car, pulling their caravan, drove past.

In the afternoon, the school children went to look at the Station yard, but the O'Malley's space was empty. The O'Malleys had really gone! They all hoped that the travelling children might return next year at the lambing season.

Prayer:

> Father God, we thank you, that you love all children.
> Help us to realise that we must be kind
> to other children, who may be strangers.
> May we welcome them as friends.
> May we never make another child unhappy,
> by anything that we may do or say.
> Through Jesus Christ our Lord.   Amen.

Hymn:

> I am planting my feet in the footsteps. (C&P.2. 103)
> or, I have decided to follow Jesus. (JP. 98)

Teachers' Note: (1) The O'Malley children were thought to be different from the other children. Were they? (2) The school children were taught many things by the O'Malleys. What did you learn? (3) What little courtesies did the O'Malleys show to the school children and their teacher? (They were invited to their caravan. They were shown the two horses. They had tea and biscuits.)

(c) The Man at the Pool

Week 2   Social Needs

Here is a story from St. John's Gospel which tells us, how Jesus dealt with a man in great social need. Remember that in days long ago, there were not any Doctors, or hospitals. Sometimes, Jesus healed people by appealing to their own faith. Sometimes, he just healed them because they needed it.

Jesus went up to Jerusalem at the time of the feast. There was once a large pool near the Sheep Gate in the city of Jerusalem. The pool was known as "Bethsaida". At the pool there were five columns of stone, which divided up the space into what looked like five porches.

If you ever go to Jerusalem, you might like to see the ruins of St. Anna's pool. Indeed, it may well be the actual pool mentioned in the story. In these porches a great number of sick, blind, and disabled people used to lie on the ground. These sick people were waiting for the movement of the waters, because they had a belief that it was the Angel of the Lord, who stirred the waters. They also believed that the first person who went into the pool, after the waters moved, would be instantly healed.

Now there was a man lying there, who was an invalid. Imagine his great need! He had been lying beside that pool for thirty-eight years. His problem was that when he was trying to get into the pool, someone else went in before him. So he was never healed. He remained an invalid for most of his life.

He just lay there hopelessly on his mat, day after day. Jesus looked kindly at the sick man, and then Jesus said to him in words, which sounded just like a command. "Take up your bed and walk." Immediately the man was completely cured. He picked up his mat, and walked away.

It was the Jewish Sabbath day when all this happened. When people saw this man carrying his mat on the Sabbath day, they said to him, "You should not carry your bed on the Sabbath." The man replied, "The Healer who made me well, told me to carry my mat, and walk. The man who was healed, had really no idea who Jesus was, because he had slipped away into the crowd."

Jesus met the same person again in the Jewish Temple. Jesus spoke to him. He said, "Seeing you have been made well, stop your doing wrong, or something worse may happen to you." (You must not conclude that because people are sick, that they have done evil. However, it is also true that some people could bring illness upon themselves. You could do yourself harm, if you were taking drugs illegally). By this time the man got to know Jesus, and so he could tell the people that it really was Jesus who had cured him.

Jesus once said, "People who are well do not need a Doctor, but those who are sick do. I have not come to call respectable people, but outcasts." (Mark.2:17.). Hospitals, Doctors, Nurses, Physiotherapists, Radiologists, Dentists, Pharmacologists, all help to make us well. They all share in the great work of God's healing power today. Children who work very hard at school, could also share in this work of healing the sick, when they grow up. The main point of this story is that all human beings are important to God.

Prayer:

    Good Heavenly Father, we thank you
    for the healing power of our Lord Jesus.
    We pray for all sick people in hospital.
    Grant the Doctors and Nurses the needed skills.
    We earnestly pray for all sick children.
    In your mercy heal them all.   Amen.

Hymn:

    I was lying in the roadway. (C&P.1. 88)
    or, Go tell it on the mountain. (C&P.1. 24) (JP. 65)

Teachers' Note: (1) The first mark of this man's life was his apparent hopelessness. (2) Yet Jesus had real love and concern for the man's predicament.

He healed him. (3) Jesus made the man stand up by himself, and then commanded him to carry his own mat home, to convince himself that he really was cured. Reference: St. John. Chapter 5. verses 1-14.

(a) Lettuces

During the second world war, enemy aeroplanes were bombing the cities and towns of Britain. The Education authorities decided that the children should all be sent away, to live on farms and in country villages, in case they might be killed in an air raid. So the children left the towns and found new homes in the country. They attended the village schools. People knew them as "evacuees."

The evacuee children taught the country children many things about factories, and docks, and railways. The country children taught the evacuees many more things about the countryside. The names of the birds, trees, and wild animals soon became known to all of them. A kind farmer allowed the evacuees to use a corner of his field to make a garden. They dug up the grass, and planted all kinds of vegetables, to help in the war effort.

When the harvest time arrived, the children helped the farmers to bring in the corn, barley, and wheat. Usually, they were paid two shillings every day, (ten pence coin). The children had made a trolley from a large box. They fixed two pram wheels, and an axle, on to the box. They made two handles, which were very like the shafts of a cart used by horses.

The evacuees' garden had grown a large amount of "iceberg lettuces". The children carefully pulled the lettuces up, and put them into the trolley. They wheeled them one mile down the road, to the shops in the little seaside town. Because the lettuces were a fresh green colour, the shopkeepers bought them from the evacuees. They gave them two pence for each lettuce. The evacuees were delighted to receive the money.

"What shall we do with the money?" they asked.

Sam said, "We could all go to the Cinema tonight, However, Peg rattled the money box, and she said, "Why not give it to the local children's hospital!" All the evacuees (except Bill) thought this was an excellent idea. Even though they would have liked to have gone to the Cinema. Bill was not too pleased, thinking to himself about the cowboy film he would miss seeing. They gave the tin box full of money to a lady collecting in the street, to take to the children's hospital. Next week they received a receipt, and a letter, thanking them for their kind gift.

A month later, one of the evacuees, Bill, aged eleven, was playing inside an old scrap car, which was lying behind a farm house. He slipped and cut his leg. It was a very nasty gash, and it needed stitches. The farmer rang for the ambulance.

Soon, Bill was whisked away to the same children's hospital to which the children had previously donated their hard earned money.

The Doctors and nurses soon got to work and cleaned up the bleeding gash in Bill's leg. They put seven stitches into the wound, to pull the flesh together. Bill had to remain in hospital for another week. Now, Bill changed his mind. Suddenly he was very pleased that they had given the money to the hospital. He had never realised just how soon that he would need hospital help.

Harvests work out just like that. Someone ploughs the fields, and someone sows the seed. Someone reaps the harvest, and someone buys the harvest plants to sell to the shops. The shops sell the harvest plants to customers, who use them for food on the table. God sends us the sunshine, and rain, to make the plants grow until harvest time. People are grateful for harvests.

Prayer:

> Lord of the harvest, we thank you,
> for sunshine, and for rain, for heat and for cold.
> We praise you, for Springtime, for Summer,
> and for the harvest time of Autumn.
> We thank you for farmers, gardeners, and shops.
> Lord of the harvest, we thank you.   Amen.

Hymn:

> Pears and apples, wheat and grapes. (C&P. 2. 135)

Teachers' Note: (1) Children love productive garden work, (horticulture) and working together. (2) Farmers and gardeners work hard all year round. (3) It is God who gives the sunshine and the rain. Harvests are plentiful, because they were meant to be shared.

(b) The Three Laws of Harvest   *Week 3   Harvest*

There are three laws of harvest.

(1) You must sow in order to reap. A lazy farmer who keeps his seed in the barn will never reap a harvest. A farmer who sows his seed, is sure to reap a harvest in good time. Everyone knows that you must put something in, to get something out.

Farmer Jones was a Welshman. He had a field on the side of a steep hill, near the sea. The field had very poor soil. He brought out his tractor, and ploughed up his field. Then Farmer Jones had a bright idea. He had noticed that in the Spring time, the high tides washed up a lot of sea-weed on the sea-shore. Now Farmer Jones knew that growing crops drained the soil of the good chemicals that were in the soil. He also knew that seaweed had good chemical elements such as iron in it, and that the seaweed would add proteins to the soil. He also knew that when the weather had broken up the seaweed into tiny particles, it would make the crops grow.

Farmer Jones took his tractor down to the shore, and he loaded some of the sea-weed on to his trailer. He took it back to his field, and spread the sea-weed all over his field. He repeated his actions, over and over again. Then he ploughed up the field once more, and buried the sea-weed. Next he ploughed up long drills of soil, and he sowed potatoes. Last of all, his plough covered over the potato seed with soil again.

That year it rained heavily, and the brown potato field became green, as the potato plants grew up strongly. In the month of September, Farmer Jones, took out his tractor once more, and he ploughed up his potato field. Imagine his delight, as he uncovered the soil, and he found long lines of healthy potatoes, which had grown up during the year. He was glad that he had sown his seed potatoes. He had reaped his harvest.

(2). We always reap exactly what we sow. If the farmer sows corn, he cannot reap wheat. If he sows turnips, he cannot reap cabbages. If he sows tomatoes, he cannot reap plums.

There is an old hymn which reads as follows:

Sow flowers and flowers will blossom,
Around you wherever you go.
Sow weeds, and weeds will be the harvest.
You'll reap whatsoever you sow.

This means that our good actions will bring good results, and our bad actions will bring bad results.

Farmer Jones' little girl was named Gwen. She had a packet of Sun-flower seeds. She asked her father, where would be the best place to grow her Sun-flower seeds.

Farmer Jones advised Gwen to sow them behind a wall, out of the way of the sea winds. Gwen, very carefully, sowed the big seeds facing South, to benefit from the warm sunshine. Within a few weeks her seeds had grown up a some inches.

Then, it rained and the sun shone, and her seeds grew up very quickly. Gwen was amazed to see that her sun-flowers had grown to nearly four metres high, by the month of August. "What are sun-flowers used for?" she asked farmer Jones. He answered, "The factory squeezes the oil from them. They make margarine from the oil." Gwen was very interested indeed.

(3) Usually, you reap more than you sow.

If you sow one potato, you may reap six or seven potatoes, at harvest time. A man once was driving his car along the road, behind a lorry. It was carrying a heaped up load of potatoes. Two potatoes fell off on to the road. The man, stopped his car, and picked up the potatoes. He took them home, and sowed the potatoes in two large plant pots. That year at harvest time, the two potatoes produced fourteen potatoes.

The man kept the fourteen potatoes as seed potatoes. He sowed them the following year. They produced eighty-two potatoes. He sowed them again the following year, and he now had two bags of potatoes. All the increase came from the harvest of two potatoes found on the road.

So the third rule of harvest is that usually you reap more than you sow. The Harvest is made up of sowing, growing, and mowing(cutting and gathering in). Children will understand that school life is like preparing for a Harvest. Sowing is like studying, Growing is like learning. Mowing is like getting successful results at the end of the time.

Prayer:

> Lord of the harvest, we thank you
> for Summer and Winter,
> for sunshine and for rain.
> We thank you for the hard work
> Farmers put into tilling the fields.
> We thank you for those people
> who pack and carry products of the harvest.   Amen.

Hymn:

> Thank you Lord, for this new day. (C&P.1. 32), (JP. 232)
> or, Have you heard the raindrops. (C&P.1. 2), (JP. 71)

Teachers' Note: (1) When we put in hard work, we certainly will get something out for our efforts. (2) If we sow an evil thought, we will reap an evil action. If we sow an evil action, we will reap an evil habit. If we sow evil habits, we will reap an evil character. If we sow an evil character, we will reap an evil destiny. (3) Usually when we work hard, we may be surprised by the success of our efforts.

(c) Weeds Among the Wheat   *Week 3   Harvest*

Jesus told the story about a farmer who sowed a field of wheat. When it became dark that night, the hard working farmer went to bed. Another farmer, who did not like the first farmer, came in the darkness, and he sowed weeds among the wheat

When the wheat seed began to spring up, fresh green shoots appeared. Then the weeds also began to appear. The weeds grew among the wheat. The servants of the farmer came, and reported that weeds were growing up amongst the wheat.

The farmer said, "Someone who is my enemy must have done this."

The servants said to the farmer, "Shall we go out and pull up the weeds?" "No", replied the farmer. "If you do that, then while you are pulling up the weeds, you may also do harm to the wheat. Let both the weeds, and the wheat, grow together until the harvest time. Then, I will tell the harvesters to pull up the weeds first of all, and to tie them together in bundles to be burned. After that, I will tell the harvesters to gather the wheat into my barn."

Jesus explained the harvest story as follows. The farmer who sowed the good seed, is the Lord. The field is the world in which we all live. The good seed are the children of the kingdom of God. (Everyone who has faith, and lives a good life.) The weeds are people in the world who deliberately do wicked deeds. The enemy who sowed the bad seed is anyone who opposes what is good, and encourages someone else to do wrong. The harvest is the end of the age, and the harvesters are the angels.

In this short story, first of all, there is good work. (The work of the farmer sowing wheat.) Secondly, there is evil work. (The secret work of the enemy who came in the night, and sowed weeds.) Thirdly, there is the test of time. (Harvest).

At school you can put in the good work, by really trying to enjoy your lessons, and to learn something new every day. If you watch carefully, in the world something bad happens every day. (Bullying, telling lies, cheating, and being jealous of others).

If we can recognise evil, that is a good way to avoid it. Most of all, it is as time passes that we develop a good or a bad character. Belief in the God of harvest will help you to be good, and honest. The harvest is in the future. What kind of person would you like to grow up to be?

Prayer:

> Lord of the harvest fields of this world,
> help us to realise that everything we do,
> results in a harvest, later in our lives.
> Let us be honest, and kind, and loving,
> because we want to grow up into God's people.   Amen.

Hymn:

> Who put the colours in the rainbow. (C&P.1. 12), (JP. 288)
> or, He's got the whole world in his hand. (C&P.1. 19), (JP. 78)

Teachers' Note: (1) Let us give credit for the good people and children, whom we meet every day. (2) Let us recognise what is bad for us, and avoid it. (3) Let us keep in mind that harvest plants usually grow stronger. Let us avoid doing evil, because in the long run, it may master us. Teachers will note that there is a reference to the "Devil" in the scripture passage. Whether it is appropriate to refer to "the Devil" in speaking to primary school children of tender age, is a professional teachers' decision. Reference; Matthew 13 verses 24-30 and verses 36-39.

(a) The Lonely Duckling   *Week 4   The Future*

Once, there was a large lake. The ducks and drakes swam about the lake. They enjoyed themselves. When Spring time arrived, the ducks had nests in the long grass and bushes of the little island, which was in the middle of the lake. The drakes in their beautiful coloured feathers continued to swim around the lake. The ducks in their brown feathers sat on their eggs, and hatched out their baby ducklings.

After a time, all the eggs were hatched. The ducklings were coloured, either yellow, or yellow and brown. Every one of them had webbed feet, so each duckling could swim at the edge of the lake, from a short time after they were hatched from the eggs. The ducklings swam in v-shaped lines, following after the mother ducks. The ducklings were ever so happy.

After about four weeks, one of the ducklings began to look a little different from the others. He was more of a grey colour rather than yellow. His neck also seemed to be slightly longer than the other ducklings. He began to feel that he was different when he compared himself to the other ducklings.

However, he continued to swim and to follow the v-shaped line of ducklings in the water, swimming after the mother duck. About eight weeks passed, and the duckling became ever larger. He grew even more grey feathers. His feet were much like other ducks, but his legs were much longer. His beak was now turning black. His neck was becoming longer and longer.

This duckling used to wish that he was like the other ducklings on the lake. Mother duck came up to him, and whispered to him, "Always be yourself. Do not wish to be somebody else. Everything will turn out all right in the end." The other ducklings either became brown in colour, or became gaily coloured like the drakes. The one duckling still continued to grow larger and stronger.

After a while, he began to lose his grey feathers, and a few white feathers were now beginning to grow on his back. He noticed that the grey feathers were falling out, and that they floated away on top of the water. More than a year had passed, when one day he heard the farmer say to a labourer, as he stood beside the lake. "That bird is not a duck, he looks more like a cygnet to me." The duckling wondered just what a "cygnet" was! Do you know what a cygnet is?

A few more months passed by, when one sunny day, the duckling looked at his mirror reflection in the lake. To his surprise, he did not see a duck, but rather he was looking at the reflection of a beautiful white Swan. Now, he truly looked to be a magnificent bird! It slowly dawned upon the lonely duckling's mind, that he had changed into becoming a large beautiful swan.

He flapped his large wings and he found that he could fly as well as swim. Up into the air he soared, and he had a good look at the lake below. Down he came again. He realised that he had become the most beautiful bird on the lake. Just at that moment other swans came out of the sky, and settled on the lake. At last he felt he could really be himself.

The swans mixed freely together. The ducks being smaller kept apart. The beautiful swan realised that he had grown up at last. Another lady swan, kept following him around the pond. He liked her company very much, indeed. Then one lovely golden evening, both swans stretched their wings, and flew off into the sunset. The other ducks never saw their swan friend again. Mother duck told her children, that the two swans had gone off to build their own nest somewhere, beside another lake. The two lovely white swans lived happy ever after.

Some boys and girls perhaps, think that they are not as good-looking or as clever as other children. They also realise that they are changing, and growing up, every day. If they mark their height on the wall with a pencil, they soon realise that they are growing fast. Their shoes soon become too small, and they must take a larger size. Soon they will have to leave the junior school, for the secondary school.

In the Secondary school, children change even more, and become more like grown up people. As boys and girls reach maturity, they realise that they are still the same people, yet their bodies have changed, and become stronger. They realise that being themselves, is the great adventure of growing up. God wants us to improve, and yet to be ourselves.

Prayer:

> Lord God, help us to be ourselves, as we grow up.
> Teach us the secret of having true faith in God.
> When we become aware of the changes in life,
> give us grace to grow up into wise adults.
> Through Jesus Christ our Lord.   Amen.

The Hymn:

> God who made the earth. (C&P.1 10), (JP. 63).

Teachers' Note: (1) The lonely duckling was sometimes unhappy, because he was not like the other ducks, (He was really a swan). Let us be happy to be ourselves. (2) In time, the lonely duckling changed into a beautiful swan. Children all change in life, when they become mature. (3) God can be our friend, if we pray, and have faith in Him, throughout the changing and "growing up process" of life.

(b) Surprise Roses

Week 4   *The Future*

The two girls, Heather and Fiona came with their parents to live in a small but lovely old house in Scotland. There was a walled garden. The lawn had very long grass, more like a hay-field. There was a wild looking hedge growing along the wall. The children loved the old house, but the garden was very untidy.

Dad decided that he would tidy up the garden. He bought a new lawn-mower, and soon had cut down the long grass. After repeated sessions of grass-cutting, the rough grass became a lovely green lawn. Next, Dad began to trim the hedge. It took quite a long time. After much trying, Dad decided to cut all the hedge down. He used a saw, and he cut the old hedge down, right to the ground. The hedge was thick and gnarled. It must have been at least one hundred years old. He burnt all the branches, and the job was finished.

That year was a very wet year. It rained on some days, almost every week of the Spring and the Summer. Dad could see that the old hedge was beginning to grow up again. In six months, it grew back again, just as high as it had been before. Then the family had a lovely surprise.

During the last week of June, roses began to appear on the newly sprung up hedge. By the time the month of July had arrived, Dad, and Mum, along with Heather and Fiona, counted nearly nine hundred lovely pure white roses growing in their garden hedge.

The children called them, "surprise roses," because they were unexpected roses. Dad explained that the hedge must have been as old as the house, which was more than one hundred years of age. Even though, he had cut down the branches of the hedge, the old roots were still alive, under the ground. With all the wet weather, the roots had just sprung to life again. The children were glad that the hedge turned out to be a white rose hedge.

Sometimes, we feel that we have not been doing very well, and we decide to make a fresh start. The second attempt can become a roaring success. So like the old hedge we can bloom better than we ever did before. God will help us, if we really mean it! Remember the old saying, "If at first you don't succeed, try, try, and try again."

Prayer:

Heavenly Father, show us how to grow up
healthy in our bodies.
Teach us how to grow in our understanding.
Show us how to become more like Jesus Christ.
Forgive us for wrong doing.
May our lives be renewed in kindness.   Amen.

Hymn:

Think of a world without any flowers. (C&P.1. 17), JP. 254)

Teachers' Note: (1) The renewing of the old rose hedge suggests to us that we may begin again. (2) When a family works together, they can make many changes for the good, with God's help. (A school is a sort of family). (3) Life can be full of pleasant surprises.

(c) The Disappointing Vineyard   *Week 4   The Future*

There is a passage in the Book of Isaiah, which is called,"The Song of the Vineyard." The poem is about the Lord, being like an Eastern vine-dresser. A Vine-dresser is the name given to anyone who produces grapes from vine trees in a vine-yard. Special skills are needed to grow grapes. The Lord looked upon the people of Israel, as his special vineyard. (The vine-tree has a special meaning which represents the Jewish nation).

The poem tells of how the Vinedresser began to make his vineyard. He chose to establish this vineyard on a fertile hillside, which means that the soil was very good soil. He dug it very well, and removed many of the stones. He then planted the choicest of vine-trees in the soil. A hedge was grown around the vineyard to protect it from the wind.

Next, he built a watch-tower, from which his servants could guard the vineyard.

Wild animals or thieves could easily be seen from the watch-tower. Last of all, he built a winepress. This winepress was similar to two stone baths, one which was higher than the other. When the grapes were thrown into the higher bath, the servants would walk on the grapes, to press them with their feet. The juice of the grapes would pour out, and flow through a hole in the higher bath, into the stone bath which was below it. From there, the wine was poured into stone jars.

After making all these preparations, the Vinedresser waited for several years until the vines grew mature enough to produce delicious bunches of grapes. His servants worked hard to make the vineyard a success. Sad to say, however, the vineyard trees only produced wild sour grapes, instead of the delicious sweet grapes which he had expected. The Vinedresser had waited a long time, for the vineyard to produce good grapes, but they never came. Each year only the wild sour grapes appeared on the vine trees. They could not be used for human consumption.

In the end, the owner of the vineyard realised that the vineyard would never produce the delicious grapes, for which he had hoped. Therefore, he tore down the hedge. He broke down its watch-tower. He gave up working his vineyard. Briars and thorns in future would grow up instead of vine trees. It would no longer be cultivated. The vineyard would become just a wasteland.

Isaiah explained the meaning of the story, as being that the Lord's people, in those days, who were represented by the vineyard, would never change from being bad, to being good people. There was something in their natures, which made them behave badly. They were like the vines in the story. The people were like bad grapes, just as some people today are like bad apples. We sometimes say that one bad apple in the barrel will affect the others.

The Prophet Isaiah used this story to tell the Lord's people that instead of producing good grapes, their conduct fell below God's standards. Just as the vines trees by their own nature could not produce sweet grapes, so the people because of their evil natures could not produce kind and honest conduct. If they persisted in their evil ways, the Lord would allow a foreign army to invade their country. This foreign army would carry them away captive.

The "Song of the Vineyard "teaches that hope for future days, depends on people changing their behaviour. Evil ways of living lead to a nation's destruction. Jesus also told the story of a vine tree. He said, (John 15.) "I am the vine, and you are the branches. Every branch in me, brings forth good fruit." Which means God wants us to produce good and kind deeds every day. When Tommy Shaw lay in hospital, after breaking his ankle while playing football at school, his class friends clubbed together, to buy him a big bunch of juicy black grapes. When his Mum brought them to him, Tommy's eyes glistened with pleasure. This was a kind action by Tommy's friends.

Prayer:

       Lord of the vineyard, we thank you for vine trees.
       We remember that Jesus Christ said,
       "I am the true vine, and my Father is the gardener."
       We remember that he also said,
       "I am the vine, and you are the branches."
       Grant us grace, to grow more like Jesus Christ our Lord.   Amen.

Hymn:

       And everyone beneath the vine and fig tree. (C&P.2. 149)
       or, To ev'rything, turn, turn, turn, (C&P.2. 113)

Teachers' Note: (1) The story of the vineyard (Isaiah Chapter 5 verses 1-6.) teaches us that good people may deteriorate and become bad. (2) The poor fruit was a disappointment to the Vinedresser. Do our lives cause God any disappointment? (3) We may plan our lives, along with others, to produce good behaviour and faith, to live useful lives in future.

(a) Falling Asleep   *Week 5   Duty*

One dark night, long ago, an old soldier in the British army named John Hatfield, was on sentry duty, at Windsor Terrace in London. John Hatfield was accused by his Officers, of falling asleep while on guard duty. The penalty for sleeping while on guard, in those days, was to be shot at dawn. First, the army Court had to be held. This Court is known as a "Court Martial". John Hatfield denied that he had ever fallen asleep on guard duty.

When the Court Martial was in session, John Hatfield, dressed in his splendid red army uniform, stood to attention. He was the Accused Person in the dock. The Prosecutor read the charge, "That John Hatfield, while being on guard duty, did fall asleep at his post, and thereby put his fellow soldiers in danger."

"How can you prove that you were not asleep on this guard duty", the Judge asked him. John Hatfield replied, "Sir, on that night, I heard the clock of St. Paul's Cathedral strike thirteen." When the Court Martial officials heard John make this statement, they said, "Clocks do not strike thirteen." Other witnesses were brought in to the Court Martial. Each of the witnesses declared, that they also had heard the clock of St. Paul's Cathedral strike thirteen.

The Judge was not satisfied with this strange story about the faulty clock in St. Paul's Cathedral. He sent Court Officials that very night, to listen to the clock. When all was dark, the Court Officials listened at twelve o'clock midnight to St. Paul's Cathedral clock. All at once, the great clock slowly began to strike, one, two, three, four, five, six, seven, eight, nine, ten, eleven, twelve ... pause ... and then thirteen, sure enough! The clock was indeed, faulty! The Court witnesses reported back to the Judge. So John Hatfield was proved to be right. He really had been awake and alert, while on guard duty.

The Judge declared that John Hatfield was not guilty of the charge brought. He was set free, and continued to be a good reliable soldier, until he was honourably discharged, years later. His good memory had saved him. His intelligent counting of the clock's bells striking thirteen, had saved his life.

Whatever else, he was doing, he certainly could not have been asleep. The witnesses had confirmed that he was telling the truth. Someone would need to see that St. Paul's clock was repaired by an expert clock-maker. John Hatfield later lived to be 102 years of age. He died in the year 1770, during the reign of King William III, and Queen Mary.

Here is another story about three people who really did fall asleep. When Jesus was praying in the Garden of Gethsemane, he asked, Peter, James, and John to pray, and to watch with him. It was a dark night. The three disciples were so tired, that their eyes shut, and they fell asleep. Jesus prayed to his heavenly Father, "Let this cup pass from me." (Meaning let the cruel cross pass from me). However, Lord, let it not be what I want, but what your wish is for me."

When Jesus discovered that his three friends had fallen asleep, he said to them, "Could you not watch one hour with me?" Just then, the Jewish officers came with lanterns, and arrested Jesus in the Garden. Peter, James and John had fallen asleep, while on guard duty. The three disciples must have felt that they had failed the Lord Jesus in his greatest hour of need. The officers took Jesus away to the Court. Jesus was sentenced to die on a cross.

We have heard two stories, one about a soldier who was accused falsely of falling asleep. The second story was about three good men, Peter, James, and John, who really did fall asleep, when they ought to have been awake.

Prayer:
>Lord God, teach us to be awake and alert,
>when we are doing our duty.
>We thank you for sleep at the end of the day.
>We thank you for the refreshment that sleep brings us.
>Guard us, and keep us safe.   Amen.

Hymn:
>Praise him in the morning. (C&P.1. 40), (JP. 202)

Teachers' Note: (1) John Hatfield was a good soldier, he did not fall asleep, while on guard duty. (2) Peter, James and John, failed Jesus, in his hour of need. They fell asleep. Some children may fall asleep in class, because they have stayed up far too late on the evening before, watching television. (3) Early to bed, early to rise, makes a man healthy, wealthy, and wise!

(b) The Little Dutch Hero   *Week 5   Duty*

If you ever go to Holland, just remember that Holland is only one part of the Netherlands. The Netherlands is a country divided from the sea. Dykes, which are sea-walls, are built to keep the sea out. Any remaining sea water is pumped out. The land inside the walls is then used for farming fields, or building sites for houses, schools, factories, and churches.

Often, the water is enclosed as well as the land. This is a clever way of providing calm fishing lakes for the fishing boats of the Netherlands. The Dutch people can always buy fresh fish for food. There are thousands of canals to drain the land, and to keep it dry. At high tide, the sea is sometimes higher than the land, so the sea-dykes have to be kept strong and secure, to prevent the sea sweeping back over the fields and towns.

Hans, was a little Dutch boy. His mother was a widow woman, whose husband had died sometime earlier. Hans had no Father to guide him. (Many children are in this position today). He had been sent to visit his old aunt. He carried a bottle of fresh milk for her. His mother told Hans, "Do not waste any time, as it gets dark early in the Winter." Hans hurried off to his old aunt, and delivered the bottle of milk. On his way home he had to walk alongside the sea-dyke.

As he walked along, he heard running water. Hans had been warned that he was to report any sign of running water to the authority of the town. The reason for this was that once the stormy sea makes a small hole in a sea-dyke, the waves would soon make it bigger. The sea would rush over the low shore, and drown all the people, their farms, and their animals.

Hans knew that it was getting dark soon. He looked carefully, and he saw that the sea was pouring through the sea-dyke in just one small hole. He knew that in an hour or so, the hole could become a hundred times bigger. He pushed his hand into the hole and his hand just about filled the hole, and of course, it stopped the sea flowing into the fields.

Hans thought to himself, "If I stay a little while, some older person will miss me, and come to my rescue. I dare not let the hole become any larger in the darkness." Hans kept holding his hand in the dyke hole, and kept the sea out. The cold wind was getting stronger. Hans' mother thought that because Hans had not arrived home, that Hans was staying overnight with his aunt. She did not worry when he had not returned. He had often stayed overnight with his aunt.

Hans felt very cold now, because he had been wearing only a thin coat. After a while, he fell asleep, still holding out the sea, with his hand in the hole. All that night no-one came to his rescue. Hans became so cold that he died during the darkness.

Next day, a search party of farmers, went out to look for Hans, when it was discovered that he had not stayed over-night with his aunt after all. They soon found Hans' frozen body, with his hand in the hole in the sea-dyke. When they took his hand out, the sea rushed through again.

The farmers put stones into the hole, and repaired the dyke.

Hans mother was heart-broken, when she realised that her darling little boy had died in the cold darkness of Winter. At the Funeral Service, held in the Dutch village Church, the Minister read the funeral Service. The Minister said, that

Hans had been a very brave boy, and that he had both saved the people, and their farms, from being washed away by the sea. He read a verse from the Bible, about Jesus on the cross. The verse he quoted said, "He saved others, himself he could not save."

No one really knows whether this traditional story is true or not. Maybe it was told to make sure that Dutch children realise the danger of allowing the dykes to leak.

Prayer:

> Heavenly Father, we thank you for every story
> of courage and bravery.
> Help us to remember that Jesus Christ our Lord,
> died for us on the cruel cross of Calvary.
> He saved others, himself he could not save.   Amen.

Hymn:

> There's a child in the streets. (C&P.1. 27)
> or, Mr. Noah built an ark. (JP. 167)

Teachers' Note: (1) Hans was intelligent enough to know the danger of water bursting through the sea-dyke. (2) In this story, Hans really died to save everyone in the district. (3) When Christians tell the story of Jesus dying on the cross, they mean that by dying, Jesus was showing God's love for everyone in the whole wide world. St. John Chapter 3 verse 16.

(c) Mary, the Mother of Jesus   *Week 5   Duty*

Mary, the mother of Jesus performed her duty. She was one of the bravest women who ever lived. She had a very difficult life. Her husband, Joseph, was a poor man. He was the village carpenter. An angel appeared to Mary, and told her that she was going to have a baby boy, and that she was to give him the name of "Jesus". This baby was to be a special baby, because he would be known as, "the Son of the most high."

Mary and Joseph were on a journey, when Jesus was about to be born. Mary gave birth to her baby in a stable, because there was no room in the Hotel. Angels sang in the dark sky to the shepherds watching over their flocks of sheep in the fields. The shepherds came to Bethlehem to see the baby Jesus.

Three Wise men from the East also travelled to see the baby born to be a King. They said that they had been guided to the village of Bethlehem, by a bright star.

Mary wondered about her baby, when both the shepherds and the wise men worshipped him, and brought him gifts. Most of the time, she kept these thoughts to herself.

Later on in her life, Mary remembered that when Jesus was twelve years old, they had been visiting the city of Jerusalem for the Jewish Feast. On the way home, they found that they had lost Jesus. It was as if a family today went on a bus-trip, and after coming back, they found that one of their children was missing. Mary and Joseph had to turn back, and journey back again to Jerusalem to search for Jesus. They found the lost boy in the Jewish Temple, learning from the Doctors of the religious Law. Jesus would have loved to attend this school. He was a good student.

Mary knew that her son Jesus was a unusual boy, full of the love of God. There is a period of about eighteen years, of which we know nothing about Jesus. However, all that time, Mary cared for Jesus along with her other children. Mary knew that Jesus loved her as his mother with all his heart. She probably would warn him not to cut himself on his father's (Joseph) sharp wood-working tools.

One famous artist has painted a picture of Jesus as a boy in his father's workshop. The sun is shining as a bright beam through the window into the dark workshop. It is evening, and the boy is stretching out both his arms, as if he was tired. The ray of the sun, makes the shadow of a cross on the wall behind Jesus. The artist wants us to know, that the shadow of the cross was over the life of Jesus, even when he was a little boy. For all the years of his boyhood, mother Mary would watch Jesus her son with a deep understanding. There was something deep, loving and good about Jesus. Mary had been chosen by God to care for him.

When Jesus was thirty years of age, he left his mother, Mary's house, and went about preaching and healing sick people. He once said, "The foxes have holes, and the birds have nests, but the Son of man has nowhere to lay his head." By this, he meant that he was a travelling preacher. He had no house of his own.

Mary would hear what people were saying about her son. They described him as a Rabbi, (religious teacher), healer, a prophet, and a good man. Mary knew that her son went about doing good. When Jesus was arrested, and then tried in a Court, she listened to the sad news.

Jesus had been condemned to carry the cross-beam of his cross, after being whipped by the soldiers, Mary was watching in the street, as Jesus passed by on his way to the hill, outside the city wall, known as "Calvary." When he was nailed to the cross, John bravely stood alongside her.

When Jesus was hanging on the cross in great pain, he looked and saw his mother standing nearby. He also saw the apostle John. He said in the accustomed manner of speaking in those days, "Dear Woman. Here is your Son." He spoke to

John, "Here is your Mother." From that time, John took Mary into his own home and cared for her.

Mary would be the happiest person in the world, when she heard that Jesus had risen from the dead. She believed that Jesus was alive, when she heard that Jesus had appeared to the eleven disciples. She would not have been surprised, because she knew that the blessing of God, was upon Jesus, even before he had been born. The angel already had shared the secret with her. Jesus could not have had a better Mother, because she had been specially chosen by God himself.

Everyone can serve God is some way. We all have our talents. Mary's duty was to care for Jesus, even before he was born. She had the task of feeding her little son, and clothing him. She would bathe him, and keep him perfectly clean. She would teach him many things about the scriptures. She would see that he was well fed. Above all, she would love him.

Everyone has an opportunity of serving God. Jesus himself said that if we give food to hungry people, or help the sick people, or visit people in prison, we are doing a service unto God himself. Any kindness shown to someone else, is a way of serving God.

Prayer:

    Lord, we thank you for the faith of Mary,
    the mother of our Lord Jesus.
    We give thanks for your special blessing on her life.
    We remember her sorrow, when Jesus was crucified.
    We give you thanks for her brave heart.   Amen.

Hymn:

    The Virgin Mary had a baby boy. (C&P.2. 121), (JP. 251)

Teachers' Note: (1) Mary had faith in God, even before Jesus was born. (2) Mary must have been grieved, when people rejected Jesus, and the soldiers nailed him on a cross. (3) Mary had God's special blessing on her life. She above all had real faith, and a brave heart.

(a) The Organist and the Artist

Allister and Andrew both went to the same school. Allister came from a family which was well off. Allister's father was the local Dentist. Andrew's family were just ordinary working people. His father was an engineer in the aircraft factory. Allister seemed to have the best of everything. He was good at most school subjects, and he could even play the piano.

Andrew was just an ordinary scholar in most subjects. However, when it came to art lessons, Andrew was very happy and relaxed. He could draw anything, without having to be shown by the Teacher. He was always very fussy about how well he sharpened his pencils. Andrew liked to make his pencil sharper than anyone else's in the class.

Before he began to draw, he would raise up his pencil in his stretched-out hand, and look carefully at what he was being asked to draw. He seemed to know whether the lines to draw were running towards him and getting larger, or going away from him, and becoming smaller. No doubt about it, Andrew would grow up to be a really good Artist.

Allister used to try to draw, but he was never very good at Art work. He was secretly jealous of Andrew. He noticed also, that Andrew could write much neater, and smaller, than anyone else in the class. Anyway, Allister thought to himself, I am cleverer than Andrew, because I always get top marks for most subjects. Yet, he had always that little niggling feeling of jealousy against Andrew's work in the Art lessons.

The two boys grew up, and left the Primary School, and both passed through the Secondary School. When the boys were eighteen years of age, Allister went off to the College of Music. Andrew went off to study Art at the University. Four Years later, Allister graduated in Music, and became second Organist at the Cathedral. He was very proud of his achievements. He felt that he had done well in life.

The Cathedral was to have several new stained glass windows installed near the Organ. One morning, Allister was playing the organ at his reversal for the next service in the Cathedral, when the workmen arrived to install the new stained glass windows. There was a young man in charge of the glaziers. He had grown long hair. He wore a bow tie. Soon, he was giving orders to the other men about the new windows.

Allister looked at the young man, and suddenly he recognised him as his old school friend, Andrew. "Fancy meeting you here. I haven't seen you for years!" said Andrew. The two young men laughed together, and warmly shook each other by the hand.

Andrew had become an Ecclesiastical Artist, which means, an Artist who makes designs for decorating Churches. He had designed, and painted the new stained glass windows for the Cathedral. Allister said to him, "You will become famous, Andrew, if you draw like you used to draw in school!"

Later on, áfter the new windows were fitted into place, and when Alister played the organ, often he would glance at the two stained glass windows in the Cathedral. They were close to the organ. One was a picture of David playing his harp. The other was a picture of Jonathan shooting with his bow and arrow beyond a stone marker. (David and Jonathan had been best friends).

Allister was never jealous of Andrew again. He realised that everyone has some special gift. His own gift was music. Andrew's talent was design and painting. Often, when Allister was playing the organ, people would look up at the stained glass windows. The window pictures helped them to worship, just as much as the organ music helped them. He realised that both of them were needed in the service of God. Just as every girl and boy in this assembly have skills that they may use in God's world.

Prayer:

Heavenly Father, we thank you for schools and learning.
We thank you for any special talents we may have.
We ask you to help us to work hard at school,
so that we may improve our learning,
and that we may become useful people,
Free from all jealous thoughts.   Amen.

Hymn:

Who put the colours in the rainbow. (C&P.1. 12), (JP. 288)

Teachers' Note: (1) Everyone is different. Each of us has some gifts that we may develop, just like Allister and Andrew. (2) Allister was jealous of Andrew's special talent of art work. (Despite his own ability at music). (3) Everyone has to play their part in the world, when we grow up. This is why we must try our best at school.

(b) The Birthday Card   *Week 6   Jealousy*

Sally and Lucy were in the same class at the primary school. Sally was very jealous of Lucy, because she was taught by an Elocution Teacher on one evening every week. Lucy did not mean to show off, but she would have loved to become a television announcer when she grew up. She was interested in reciting poetry. She would practise, saying, "aaaa ! eeee ! iiiii! oh ! oooo."

At other times Lucy would repeat to herself in the playground, "How, now, brown cow." Lucy was learning how to pronounce her vowels correctly. Sally did not bother how she spoke, so she thought that Lucy just was being proud and conceited. Sally really was jealous of Lucy, her school friend.

When Lucy's birthday came round, Sally decided to send Lucy a nasty birthday card. She bought the birthday card at the shop near the school. Sally began to think hard. Then she wrote inside the card ...

> Lucy has floppy ears and a big nose.
> She has flat feet, and horrible toes.
> She says everything so polite.
> She talks too much, by day or night.

Sally did not sign her name to the Birthday card. She sent it off in a stamped envelope in the post. When it arrived at Lucy's home, on her birthday morning, Lucy was a was most upset. All the other cards were lovely greeting cards. She wondered who might have sent the nasty birthday card. Someone must be very jealous to write such a verse.

Now, Lucy was really a kind-hearted girl, and she never held a grudge against anyone. That day in school, she looked at Sally's handwriting, and immediately, she knew that it was Sally, who had written the nasty birthday card. Lucy did not say to Sally, that she had found her out. She tried to be helpful to Sally. Lucy had put off her birthday party for two weeks, because her father was away overseas on business. She would hold the party when he came home.

That morning, the Teacher asked Lucy to read, William Wordsworth's poem about the Daffodils. Lucy read the poem as well as she could. She really tried her best to give meaning to the verse. She read,

> I wandered lonely as a cloud
> That floats on high o'er vales and hills,
> When all at once I saw a crowd,
> A host of golden daffodils;
> Beside the lake, beneath the trees,
> Fluttering and dancing in the breeze.

Lucy read the verse so well, that all the children could see the Daffodils in their minds. She was wonderful! When her birthday came round, and Lucy's father had come home again, Lucy decided to send Sally a lovely invitation card. She chose the nicest card that she could find. Lucy wrote inside the card, "Please, come to my birthday, Sally! You are most welcome. Best wishes." Then she wrote a verse, and signed her name, "Lucy."

The verse read:

Sally, we all like you, and we hope you'll be,
A happy girl for all to see.
Roses are red, and violets are blue,
and everything I say is true.
Come to my party at half-past four.
True friends cannot be jealous any more.

Sure enough, at half past four, Lucy's friends came to her birthday party. Lucy saw Sally coming to her garden gate. She ran out to make her welcome. "I am so glad that you managed to come, Sally" she said. Sally whispered, "I am sorry for what I wrote on your birthday card. I promise that I shall never be jealous ever again. The two girls became the very best of friends, and lived happy ever after.

Prayer:

Lord Jesus, take away any jealousy
that we may have in our hearts and minds.
Teach us how to value our school friends.
Show us how to return good for evil.
May our Leaders and Teachers,
also be our friends.   Amen.

Hymn:

Think of a world without any flowers. (C&P.1. 17), (JP. 254)
or, Jesus good above all other. (C&P.1. 23)

Teachers' Note: (1) Many people are better skilled than we are at many things. This is not a reason for being jealous. They can inspire us to try more. (2) When we write anything down, it becomes worse. It is better not to write, than to write unkind words. (3) Lucy showed a forgiving spirit. She returned good for evil. Sally never wrote unkind words again.

(c) Jacob and Esau   *Week 6   Jealousy*

Esau and Jacob were born as twins. The names of their Father and Mother were Isaac and Rebecca. They called the first-born child, "Esau", because he was born, with ginger coloured hair. The second-born child they called "Jacob", because, when he was born, he was holding on to the heel of the first-born child.

This name "Jacob" means "Heel-grasper" in the Hebrew language. Because the second baby was holding on to the foot of the first baby born, it looked as if the second baby wanted to be the first. It looked as he was jealous of the first baby born. Jacob was not really a nice name. In those days, people liked to name a person in a way which that would describe his or her character. That is why Jacob, the heel-grasper, received his name. It turned out to be a true description of Jacob, for he was always jealous of Esau.

When they became men, Esau became a skilled hunter, who loved the open countryside. Jacob was a quieter person, and liked to live among the tents. Esau came home from hunting one day. He was starving with hunger. Jacob had just made a pot of red lentil stew. "I am famished," said Esau, "give me some of that red stew." Jacob, saw his chance. "Sell me your birthright, Esau, and I will give you a plate of red stew." Esau thought to himself, "Here I am starving with hunger What good is the birth-right to me right now". Esau swore to Jacob, and he gave Jacob his birth-right. Jacob in turn gave to Esau some bread, and a plate of lentil stew.

Jacob knew that owning the birth-right gave him the rights of the first born son in the family. In some countries, when the father dies, the family land or farm is left to the to the eldest of the brothers. (The reason for this is to keep the family farm large.) In other countries, the family farm may be divided between all the remaining brothers. This has the effect of dividing up the land between them, and making the farm much smaller. The point here was that Esau did not live for the future, he lived for the present. The Bible says that Esau despised his birth-right. Jacob always wanted to be most important.

Some years rolled by. Isaac, the father, became very old. His eyes became weak, and finally he went blind. Isaac knew that in a short time he would die of old age. Parents should love all of their children in the same manner. In this home, it would seem that Isaac, the father, loved the elder twin, Esau, a little more, than Jacob. On the other hand, Rebecca, the mother, seemed to favour Jacob, the younger twin.

The father, Isaac, called Esau in order to speak with him. He said, "I am getting old, Esau, I do not know how soon I might die. Go out, and hunt some wild game for me. Make me a tasty meal, and bring it to me. After I eat the meal, I will pray, and give you my blessing before I die." Esau went out to hunt in the forest.

Rebekah, the mother of the two sons, had heard Isaac speaking. She called Jacob, and told him what Isaac had said to Esau. Rebekah, told Jacob, "Now is your chance. Go out to the flock of goats, and bring me two of the best young goats. I will kill the goats, and make the tastiest meal that I can make. I know just how your father likes his dinner. Then, Jacob, you take in the tasty meal to your father, and your father will bless you before he dies, instead of blessing Esau. Just do as I tell you, Jacob."

Rebekah made the lovely tasty meal. She dressed up Jacob in Esau's best clothes. She also covered Jacob's smooth hands, and neck with the goat-skins. So that Jacob's skin would appear to feel rough, like Esau's skin. Cunning Jacob carried the food into the presence of his old blind father, and gave it to him. Jacob said to his father, Isaac, "Eat up father, and then you may give to me your blessing."

Isaac ate the tasty meal. Then, the old blind father put out his hands. Old Isaac felt his son's face, and then his son's hands, which had been covered by the goat skins. The skins made Jacob's hands appear to feel hairy, just like the hands of Esau. Isaac said, "The voice is the voice of Jacob, but the hands are the hands of Esau."

Isaac asked Jacob to give him a kiss on the cheek, as is the custom in the Near Eastern countries. When Jacob came close, Isaac could smell Esau's clothes. He prayed, and gave his special blessing to Jacob. "May God bless you, and make you rich. May you be Lord over your brothers." In this way, Jacob stole his father's blessing, which had been meant for Esau.

Just after this had happened, Esau came rushing home from his hunting the wild game. He went in to Isaac, and Isaac despite being blind, realised that he had blessed Jacob, instead of Esau. Isaac told Esau that he had already made Jacob Lord over of him. That could not be changed. Jacob had stolen the elder brother's place in the family. Esau called out, "Bless me also, father!" Isaac gave Esau a blessing of lesser importance. Esau was angry against Jacob, because he felt that had been out-witted. He held a grudge against Jacob for a long time afterwards.

It is wrong to be jealous. It is also wrong to steal a birth-right. Both sons were doing something which was wrong. Maybe, Esau's fault was the greatest. He put no value on what lay in the future. (His father's dying blessing on the oldest son.) With the blessing, went the admission that person receiving it, was first in the family. Jacob having been born a twin, seemed to want that value more than anything.

Prayer:

> Good Lord, help us not to be jealous of others.
> Teach us that jealousy is sinful.
> Help us to be kind to our school friends.
> Bless all children everywhere.
> Make the sick well again, and the sad children happy.   Amen.

Hymn:

> I belong to a family, the biggest on earth. (C&P.1. 69)

Teachers' Note: (1) Jacob was always jealous of Esau. Jacob always felt that he was a second class person. (2) Isaac's favourite was Esau, while Rebekah's favourite was Jacob. Parents should love all the family in an equal manner, and never have a favourite son or daughter. (3) God had yet to change Jacob's greedy nature. (His name was later changed to "Israel." Ref. Genesis Chap. 27.)

(a) Guru Nanak

Introduction. People who believe in Jesus Christ and follow his teaching are known as Christians. There are also people living in our country who practise other religions. One of these other "world religions" is the Sikh religion. Today we are going to hear about their traditions. The reason we do this is to help us understand each other. People of the Sikh Religion may live near us, or attend our school, or serve us in a shop. Their life-style may be different from ours, because of their religion.

Guru Nanak was the founder of the Sikh religion. He was born long ago in the year 1469 at Talwandi in Northern India. He had been born into a Hindu home. He also lived in an area where there were also many members of the Muslim religion. Sometimes the Hindus and the Muslims would not agree with each other. This used to puzzle the young boy Nanak.

Nanak's father decided that his young son, Nanak, should become an accountant, like himself. An accountant is a mathematically trained keeper of books, and business accounts, and money matters. Nanak had a good brain, and he soon learnt how to count quickly in his head.

One day, when Nanak was still only a boy, his father gave him some money. He told Nanak to buy and sell in the local town, and to do business to increase his store of money. On the way to the town, with the money in his pocket, Nanak happened to travel through a forest. There he saw a group of hungry men who were praying. They were religious men, and they had not eaten any food for about one week. The young Nanak went to the town shops. He spent his money buying baskets of food, which he carried back to the poor hungry men in the forest.

When Nanak returned to his father, his father asked his son, whether he had made any bargains, and how much money had he made. Nanak had nothing to show for his money spent. His hands and his pockets were empty. His father was angry at first. Nanak told him, "Father, you told me to do the best business I could. Father, I have fed hungry people with my money, and no one could do any better than that." Nanak's father realised that his son would grow up to be a special person. Nanak was truly a kind-hearted boy. He often thought about God.

One day Nanak went with his young friends to sit beside a river. A little later, his friends could not find him. They returned home, and thought that, perhaps, Nanak had been drowned. Three days later, Nanak came home. For one whole day he never spoke. When he did speak, he said that he would neither be a Hindu, nor a Muslim, but that he would follow God's path. He meant that for him, it did not matter which religion a person followed, as long as that person genuinely served God with all his or her heart.

A Guru is a holy Teacher in India. Nanak became the chief Guru, and was known as Guru Nanak ever since. Nanak used to tell the people, "God is the true Guru". Nanak was also a good singer, as well as a preacher. He travelled about India teaching the people about God. The word Sikh means "a Disciple." All Sikhs try to be disciples of God's good way of life.

Nanak taught that every person is of equal importance before God. That is why everyone is invited to a meal, after attending a Sikh service of worship, even though they may not be Sikhs.

Prayer:

> Lord God, we pray to you as our Heavenly father.
> We thank you that we are all God's children.
> Teach us to have faith, and live good lives.
> We pray for children in countries overseas.
> We pray for the needy children of the third world.   Amen.

Hymn:

> The ink is black, the page is white. (C&P.1. 67)

Teachers' Note: (1) Nanak became a great Guru, because he prayed to God as a boy. No one is too young to pray. (2) Nanak, when he was a boy, did not realise that he would influence so many people for the good. Our children will also grow up, and influence others, maybe as good footballers, or as honest business people, or kindly Police officers, or as a skilled Musicians. Some children are going to become trained Nurses in Hospitals. Life is an adventure. (3) Nanak believed that we are all equal in the sight of God. We are all God's children.

(b) The Five "Ks"   *Week 7   The Sikhs*

If your school has Sikh pupils attending it, then the Teacher may like to involve the Sikh children in this Assembly, with the permission of their parents. The Assembly will become very effective, and more interesting, if this course is followed.

Sikhs are some of the people who came to Britain from Western India. The men and boys are easily recognised by their wearing of a turban on their head. A turban is a piece of cloth, between two and four metres long. Sikhs have five signs by which they are known as Sikhs. They all begin with the letter "K". The turban is not one of the five "Ks".

The first sign is known as the "Kesh". The Kesh is the uncut hair. The turban is used to keep the uncut hair in place.

The second sign is known as the "Kangha." The Kangha is the comb fixed in the hair. (To hold the hair in place)

The third sign is known as the "Kaccha". The Kaccha is the pair of short trousers which all Sikh men wear. They make it easier to move about, rather than wearing long robes.

The fourth sign is known as the "Kirpan". The Kirpan is a short sword. The meaning of the Kirpan is that all male Sikhs must be willing to fight to defend truth and justice. The short sword, is really a symbol, (sign) where Sikhs have no need to fight.

The fifth sign is known as "Kara". The Kira is a bangle. All Sikhs know that the bangle is a circle, and that it has no beginning or ending. The Kara bangle, reminds the Sikhs that that they are one with God.

Young Sikh boys wear their hair in a "Topnot." They never cut their hair. When they grow older, they may wear a turban of any colour, Generally, in Britain, they wear white turbans. The Sikh women cover their hair with a scarf, which is usually made of cotton, or muslin. These head-coverings are worn by women worshippers out of respect for the Sikh place of worship, which is called the "Gurdwara."

After Guru Nanak died, there were another nine Gurus, who followed each other, in succession, until each Guru had died. The tenth Guru was known as Guru Gobind Singh. Since the Gurus are now dead, Sikhs obey a holy book, which is found in every Guardwara. The Holy Book is called the "Guru Granth Sahib", and it has a special place of respect in the Gurdwara. To be a Sikh, one must always obey the Guru Granth Sahib, which is the Sikhs' Scriptures. (Holy writings.)

Prayer:

> Lord God of the whole world,
> we pray for the Sikh people,
> and the children, who belong to that religion.
> Teach us to respect their goodness, and faith.
> We pray that the world may be at peace.
> Bless any children who are sick. Amen.

Hymn:

> All creatures of our God and king. (C&P.1. 7)

Teachers' Note: (1) The turban may be of any colour. (2) The five (Ks.) signs of the Sikh religion are to identify the witness of the Sikh faith in God. (3) The Guru Granth Sahib is the name of the Sikh Scriptures and is very important to Sikhs.

Test the children to see whether they can remember the English equivalent of the five "Ks"? (Un-cut hair, comb, short trousers, the short sword or dagger, and the bangle).

(c) The Khalsa   *Week 7   The Sikhs*

If you are born into a Sikh family, then you are a Sikh. However, Just as Christians have an initiation (a beginning) ceremony, called "baptism," so Sikhs also have a beginning ceremony called "the Amrit Ceremony." Passing through the Amrit Ceremony confirms that the young men are true believers. This is a way of joining the Sikh community, which is known as the "Khalsa."

The first Amrit ceremony was held in India, long ago, in the year 1669. Guru Gobind Singh, the tenth Guru called the Sikh people to an assembly. Guru Singh Gobind stood in front of the crowd of people, with a drawn sword in his hand. He asked the people, who would be willing to lay down his life for God.

At first, no-one made a move. Then, one young man stepped forward from the crowd. Guru Gobind Singh took the young man into the large tent, and closed the doorway. The crowd heard a noise, as if a sword had struck the young man. Guru Gobind Singh reappeared. His sword was dripping with blood. The watching crowd were shocked.

A second time, he asked the crowd, who would be willing to die for the Guru God. Another young man volunteered, and he followed the Guru into his tent. Again, the Guru re-appeared, holding his sword dripping with blood. He repeated this three more times, and each time, he took another young man into the tent, and closed the door.

After the fifth man was taken into the tent, Guru Gobind Singh, brought all the five men alive out of the tent. They were dressed just like him, in saffron (orange) coloured tunics, with blue waist-bands. The crowd realised that Guru Gobind Singh was only testing the sincerity, faith and loyalty of the young men. He had not harmed them after all. (Sikhs believe this to be a true part of their history).

These five men, became known as, "the Beloved Five". They were given "Amrit" to drink, (which is a mixture of sugar crystals and water.) The Sikh men were given the name of "Singh," which means "a lion." These five men became the first members of the Khalsa, the Sikh community. (Sikh women are known by the name of "Kaur" which means, "Princess".) These five Sikh men had dedicated themselves to defending their faith and the poor and needy of any religion.

All Sikhs have the surname of "Singh", to show that they all belong to one large family. The most famous of the Sikh Temples is the Golden Temple of Amritsar in the Punjab in India.

Prayer:

> Lord of all the earth, bless all your people, everywhere.
> Teach all people of the world to live together in peace.
> Bless all Sikhs here in Britain.
> Be near all Sikh boys and girls.
> Show us how to be good friends to each other.   Amen.

Hymn:

> I've got peace like a river. (C&P.2. 143), (JP. 120)

Teachers Note: (1) Guru Gobind Singh wanted to test the witness of his Sikh believers. Were they willing to die for the Sikh faith? (2) Not all Sikhs pass through the Amrit ceremony. Some delay initiation (beginning) for a longer time. (3) The Sikh scriptures, (holy book) known as the Guru Granth Sahib, are treated by Sikhs as a "living Teacher". (Word of God). Today, Sikhs need our respect.

(a) Edinburgh Time   Week 8   Usefulness

Here is an old story which was sometimes told to visitors, by the people who lived in Edinburgh. The Edinburgh folk, sometimes have the gift of laughing at themselves. There is a beautiful street in Edinburgh, called Princess Street. It is lined with shops on one side of the street, and on the other side, there are civic gardens, monuments, and the Art gallery. In the gardens there is a magnificent large flower clock. Visitors come from all over the world to see the flower clock. The Edinburgh castle overlooks both Princess Street and the gardens. At one o'clock each day, the soldiers in the castle, fire off a gun, which makes a very loud bang.

A little boy named Hamish asked the Captain of the Guard, at the castle, how the Gunners knew the exact time to fire off the gun. The Captain said, that he always chose a soldier, who was a very good runner, to put on his running shorts and jersey, wearing a wrist watch. The soldier had to run down from the castle to a shop in Princess Street. This particular shop sold beautiful jewellery, alongside clocks, and watches. In the window of this shop, there was another large clock, which always told the exact time, to the correct second. It was said, that the clock had never lost a moment in one hundred years.

The soldier would arrive at the shop and look at the clock in the window, and then, he would adjust his watch. Next, the soldier would run along Princess street, making his way back to the castle. When the Gunners assembled, on the wall of the castle, he would take out his watch, and exactly at one o'clock, he would raise his hand, and the Gunners fired the castle gun. Everyone in Edinburgh, on hearing the sound of the gun, would check their clocks, and watches. The Park-keeper would also adjust the flower clock, by the sound of the gun.

Little Hamish, took a walk along Princess Street, because he wanted to see the shop, with the clock, which told the perfect time. Sure enough, there it was! Hamish stared at the clock. He was thinking all the time. Then little Hamish went inside the shop, and he asked the shop-keeper, "How do you know that the clock in your shop window, keeps perfect time?" The shop-keeper, looked at little Hamish hardly believing his ears, that anyone could doubt the clock, which had told the exact time for one hundred years.

"Laddie," he said, "I wait until I hear the castle gun firing at one o'clock every day, and then I adjust my clock in the shop window." Hamish, smiled at the shop-keeper, and politely said, "Thank You." Hamish was a thinker! He thought to himself, the Edinburgh people are taking the correct time from each other, and they do not know it. If the castle gun is slow or fast, then the shop clock will be wrong.

On the other hand, if the clock in the shop is slow or fast, then they will fire off the castle gun at the wrong time. That means that everyone in Edinburgh, is likely to have the wrong time anyway. Hamish, said that Edinburgh was a lovely city, but some things were difficult to understand. He went off back home to Aberdeen, where they always tell the time by the radio. (Greenwich Time).

This is a funny story, which Edinburgh people tell against themselves. Did you see what the story meant. We watch each other, and so often, we copy each other.

Have you ever watched someone in your class yawn? Do not say a word, but watch how many others in the class, also begin to yawn. Often, they do not know that they are unconsciously copying other people. Young people like to wear the same kind of trainers as everyone else wears in the school. We adopt the habits we see in others, therefore, we must be on our guard, because what others do, may not always be good manners. What others do may not always be honest. What others do may not be what we want to do. As we grow older in the school, we have to try to set a good example, in sport, in learning, and in good behaviour to the younger members of the school.

Many people set us a good example. These are the people we ought to follow, if we want to be a success in life. Jesus is the best example that we could ever have. He did no evil. He was never unkind. If everyone in my school were just like me. What kind of a school, would my school be?

Prayer:

    Father, God, teach us to follow
    the example of the Lord Jesus.
    Keep us honest and kind.
    Make us to be "good-sports,"
    and hard workers at our school studies.
    Teach us that the world is watching us.   Amen.

Hymn:

I am planting my feet in the footsteps. (C&P.2. 103)

Teachers' Note: (1) Edinburgh people can laugh at themselves. Is this difficult for some children? (2) We fix many of our habits, by imitating others. (3) To set a good example requires a strong will, and inward strength of character.

(b) Charlie's Walking Stick   *Week 8   Usefulness*

(Teachers' note. A walking stick would be a useful object lesson at the beginning of this story.)

"I am a walking stick. Let me tell you something about myself. I once was part of a blackthorn hedge growing around Mr. Charlie Currie's field. (A blackthorn is also known as the "Sloe Bush." The Latin name is Prunis Spinosa). Blackthorns may grow beside hawthorn bushes, but you will know the blackthorn because the bush has very straight strong branches, with a black bark, and it also grows large thorns very like long spikes.

I am not being disrespectful, but everyone calls Mr. Currie, "Charlie Currie," and since he is my best friend, why should I not call him "Charlie Currie," just like everyone else? Charlie was walking round the edges of his largest field, when he stopped, where I was growing in the hedge. He said to himself, "There is a splendid branch of blackthorn. It is as straight as a small flag-pole and as strong as steel. I think that I will have that blackthorn branch for my own use.

Away he went. Soon, Charlie came back with a saw, and a bill-hook in his hands. He sawed down the branch, which was me, and then he used his bill-hook, (a hedge-chopper) to cut off all the small side thorn branches growing out of me. "There," he said to himself. "What a beautiful walking stick this branch will make."

Later, I was held in a bench vice, smoothed down with a carpenter's plane, and I became just like any other walking stick, which was being made. Except that I knew that I was stronger than they were! Then, he kept putting me into hot water, and under a steam jet, until he bent part of me into a curved handle at one end. At the other end, he put a little brass ring, and hammered it on tight. Last of all he varnished me all over, and hung me up to dry. I looked really splendid that day. I had become Charlie Currie's best friend. I was his very own walking stick.

I accompanied Charlie everywhere he went. He was very proud of me. He showed me to his friends, and also to the village Priest. When one of the new Spring lambs was frolicking and gamboling about, it fell into the ditch, which was filled with dirty water. Charlie used my curved handle, to put round the little lamb's tummy, and soon he pulled out the wet lamb.

Charlie carefully carried the lamb back to the other two hundred sheep, which were grazing in the field. The lamb bleated, and one of the ewe sheep, immediately ran over to the lamb, which it had recognised as its own. Both mother and son trotted away down the field. All is well that ends well!

Charlie brought me, when he visited Widow Wilson, whose husband, Tom, had been killed in the war. Charlie also brought Widow Wilson, a cabbage, a lettuce, and half- a-dozen eggs, because Tom had been his best friend. Charlie tried to take care of widow Wilson. When her dog would not let him inside the gate, he used me, his walking stick, to fend the dog off him. Then, he knocked her door, and opened it. Soon, the dog would became calm again.

If Charlie was tired, he always rested on me. If Charlie was pointing anything out, he always used me to show the direction he meant. Charlie never talked to himself, he always talked to me, instead. He would say,"You are my best friend, young fellow, you never let me down, and you never tell any of my secrets. I wish that everyone was as reliable as my walking stick."

Charlie used to say the twenty-third Psalm to himself. "The Lord is my Shepherd, I shall not want. He leads me beside the still waters. He restoreth my soul. He leads me in the paths of righteousness for his name's sake. Yes, even though I walk through the valley of the shadow of death, I will fear no evil. For you are with me. Your rod and your staff strengthen me". Then he would stop. He would say, *"That rod and staff* part just means that every shepherd needs a walking stick."

Have you ever noticed that a Bishop carries a shepherd's crook, about with him, on his official visits. A shepherd's crook after all, is only a large walking stick. It is the badge of his office. The congregation are his flock. When the Bishop is first installed in his Cathedral, before he enters, he knocks on the cathedral door, three times with his shepherd's crook.

We all should be like Charlie Currie's walking stick. He was straight and honest. He was useful. He was a pointer. He was willing to bear the load of any tired walker on the path of life. He was strong enough to keep off an excited dog. He went on good errands with Charlie, to take care of Widow Wilson, and to give her a little extra to eat. Best of all, he was a reliable, trustworthy friend. That is why Charlie Currie always loved his walking stick.

Prayer:

> Lord, our Heavenly Father,
> make us all reliable, and trustworthy.
> Help us to make life easier for other people.
> Bless everyone who needs a friend,
> or a shepherd, or a guide.
> Teach us not to fail them.   Amen.

Hymn:

My faith it is an oaken staff. (C&P.1. 46), (JP. 168)

Teachers Note: (1) The important fact is that Charlie Currie chose the blackthorn branch himself. (2) The walking stick needed to be cut and shaped in order to become a useful object. Education is to prepare us for our part in this world. Like the removal of thorns, learning removes false ideas, and shapes our thinking. (3) The walking stick accompanied Charlie everywhere, and carried his weight, when he was tired. We also can help others.

(c) Paying Taxes

Week 8   Usefulness

If you have a coin in your pocket, take a good look at it, before you begin. Questions; Can you read its value? Can you tell which King's or Queen's image is on the coin. Can you tell from the reverse side of the coin, whether the inscription represents, Scotland, England, Wales, or Northern Ireland? If your coin is genuine it may have a date upon it some where. "D. G." means "by the Grace of God." "Reg" means "Queen" and "D", "F" means "Defender of the Faith".

The Pharisees, who were the strict Jewish Leaders, decided to lay a trap for Jesus. They decided that they would ask Jesus a trick question, so that he might be caught speaking against Caesar, the Roman Emperor. Then, they could report the answer to the Roman rulers, and Jesus would be arrested, and killed. They were trying to ensnare Jesus in his talk.

The Pharisees gathered round Jesus and asked him, What do you think? Is it lawful to pay taxes to Caesar, or not?" Jesus answered, "You hypocrites, why are you trying to trap me? Let me look at the coin with which you pay the tax. They brought a Denarius, a small Greek coin, to Jesus. Jesus looked at the coin, and he asked them, whose image was on the coin, and whose inscription was on the coin? The Pharisees replied that it was Caesar's image (face), and it was Caesar's inscription which was on the coin. Jesus said, "Give to Caesar that which belongs to Caesar, and give to God, that which belongs to God."

Have you ever realised that you may do a lot of good with money, or you could do a lot of evil. It is true that most people must pay some form of taxes or rates. We may have to pay rent for a house, or water rates for our tap-water. Our parents may have to pay National Insurance, to pay for the hospitals and Doctors. They may even pay income tax to keep the government going. They also pay for schools and education. (Giving unto Caesar, means giving money to the Government to pay the expenses of running the country).

That is a useful way to use our money. We could give money to Christian Aid for overseas help. We could occasionally give money to the sick animals' dispensary. We could give money to God and his church. We could give something to someone who has less that we have. We could put money into an envelope, for charity, which is collected around our doors.

On the other hand we could waste our money. We could buy selfish treats for ourselves. For instance, we could be greedy and buy for ourselves two bottles of lemonade, when we only need one. We could gamble our money away, and get nothing in return. We could become careless, and even lose our money.

There is a third way of dealing with our money. We could lend it. When we put money in the saving's bank, we are actually lending our money to the bank. Once each year, the bank pays us for our loan of money, by awarding us "Interest".

It might be £5.00 for every £100 we have kept in the account. If you had £50 in the account, then you might be given £2.50 interest at the end of the year. (£50.00 plus £2.50 adds up to £52.50. It soon begins to increase.

Dr. Barnardo collected money from other people to build homes for Britain's orphan children. Christian Aid helps many countries' poor hungry people. The Salvation Army collect money for the Social needs of others. Catholic Aid helps poor third world people. John Wesley used to tell Methodists. "Earn all you can. Save all you can. Give all you can."

Prayer:

>Heavenly Father, help us to use our money wisely.
>Help us to support good causes.
>May we not forget to give to God's church.
>Teach us to be helpful to charities.
>We pray especially for poor people.
>We pray for the children of the third world.   Amen.

Hymn:

>When I needed a neighbour, were you there. (C&P.1. 65), (JP. 275)

Teachers' Note: (1) We own a duty to God and to Caesar. (The church/needy people, and to the State). (2) Children are beginning to learn the value and usefulness of money. Let us be wise. (3) Money wisely used may bless the world.

(a) R. L. Stevenson's Epitaph

Mary and Richard were school-children, who had an interest in church graveyards. Sometimes the graveyards which they inspected, were over-run with long grass. They knew that one Vicar in North Yorkshire keeps the grass short, by allowing a local farmer to graze his sheep in the Church-yard. The sheep ate the grass between the old head-stones. The graveyard was kept neat and tidy.

Mary, and Richard, each carried little notebooks with them. They wrote down strange and interesting things which they saw in the graveyard. They read one headstone, which had an inscription written upon it. The words were,

Remember friend as you pass by,
as you are now, so once was I.
As I am now, so soon you will be.
Prepare then friend, to follow me.

The children did not think that these words were mournful. They agreed that probably the person who died, wanted everyone to realise that this life was a short one, and that everyone should be happy and worship God, while they are alive.

The two children heard a new teacher at school tell them about Robert Louis Stevenson, who lived in Edinburgh (1850-94). He was a wonderful author of books and poems for young people. He wrote books, such as, "Kidnapped", and "Treasure Island." He wrote such poems as, "Windy Nights." He also wrote a book of poems called "A Child's Book of Poems." He was often referred to just as R.L.S., he was so well known.

The new teacher told the children, that Stevenson married an American lady. Sad to relate, Stevenson suffered from Tuberculosis; the silent disease. In those days, many children and adults caught Tuberculosis, (or T.B. as it was called as a short common name). The T.B. germs came from cows. People everywhere drank cow's milk, and so they too caught the disease.

The disease wasted people's health away, until they were thin and weak. They finally died. Farmers later were encouraged to raise Tubercular Free herds of cows. The disease died out among the cattle. Then Sir Andrew Flemming, discovered that penicillin elements killed the T.B. germs. At last the Doctors found that they could easily cure people suffering from T.B. by using injections of Penicillin. Next time you see a milk bottle or carton, look for the T. T. sign on it.(Tubercular Tested).

In those old days, Robert Stevenson knew that he was slowly dying. He went on a sailing holiday to the South Sea Islands. It was such a beautiful place, that Stevenson and his wife decided to remain there with the native people of Samoa. The Samoan Islands enjoyed fresh air, and lovely warm weather. There were sandy beaches and high mountains.

Stevenson thought that the change of climate would help him to get well again. The native people loved him, and they honoured him as their chief. (A title of honour, which they gave him). Sad to say R. L. Stevenson died. His body was carried in a funeral procession of sixty Samoan people, to the top of a very high mountain. It is possible to see the rolling blue waves of the Pacific Ocean, from Stevenson's lonely grave on the mountain top.

The new Teacher surprised the children, by telling them, that during the time, when their own parents went to school, they were often taught to recite Robert Louis Stevenson's epitaph. (An "epitaph" is an inscription carved on a tombstone, over someone's grave). Stevenson had written his own epitaph. These words are inscribed on his tombstone on the island of Samoa. Many children know it off by heart. It reads,

> "Under the wide and starry sky.
> Dig the grave and let me lie.
> Glad did I live, and gladly die.
> And they laid me down with a will.
> This be the verse you *grave* for me.   (write on my headstone).
> Here he lies where he longed to be.
> Home is the sailor, home from the sea.
> and the hunter home from the hill."

There was once a written inscription on a placard nailed on the top of the cross where Jesus died. It read, "This is Jesus of Nazareth, King of the Jews"

Christians do not need an epitaph over the grave of Jesus, because Christians believe that Jesus arose from the grave on the first Easter Sunday. The messenger said to the disciples, "Why are you seeking the living among the dead. He is not here, he is risen."

Prayer:

> Lord our Father in Heaven,
> we thank you for the life, and
> for the written words of Robert Louis Stevenson.
> Bless all children's authors,
> that they may they write what is good and wholesome.
> Help us to read the Holy Bible.   Amen.

Hymn:

> The wise may bring their learning. (C&P.1. 64). (JP. 253)

Teachers' Note: (1) Children do come to face the fact of death. (Grand-parents). (2) Discussion of death need not be morbid. For Christians, the Resurrection of Jesus is most important. (3) Robert Louis Stevenson suffered poor health all his life, yet what wonderful stories and poems he wrote for young people. A good example of the use of time. (He originally wanted to become a civil engineer, like his father).

(b) The Friend in Need   *Week 9   Helpers*

Farmer Harris went to church every Sunday. He was very particular to keep the Lord's Day free from any work, if he could help it. Although, he had to milk the cows, and feed the hens. He tried to do only the work which he must do. Every other job, he left to Monday morning. He used to quote to anyone who asked him, "A Sunday well spent, brings a week of content." He would always say, "Sunday is a day for a happy family to enjoy."

Now Farmer Harris had a prize bull, whom they called "Harvey." One dark night, Harvey the bull, accidentally fell into the old dis-used duck-pond. Harvey was a very heavy bull, weighing more than one ton. The Bull's feet sank down into the mud of the duck pond. Next morning, Farmer Harris found that Harvey had sunk even further into the soft mud. He really was stuck so fast, that he could not get himself out. The great Bull was bellowing loudly, and getting angrier all the time.

Farmer Harris had a problem on his hands. He usually went to church, leaving at ten o'clock, in his Land Rover. The family all went together. Now he had to think matters through. The Vet was on holiday. Farmer Harris did not like missing church. He saw that his Bible was on the table from the previous evening. He picked it up to put it away, and accidentally his eyes happened to read some verses from, St. Luke chapter 14 verse 5.

It was the passage where Jesus was speaking about the Sabbath Day to the Lawyers and the Pharisees (strict Jewish religious Leaders). He said, "Which of you, who has an ox or an ass fall into a pit, will not immediately pull him out." That was the answer for Farmer Harris. He would not go to church on that day after all.

Mrs. Harris would drive her own car to church instead. Farmer Harris wondered how he could get Harvey the Bull out of the duck-pond. Jane his daughter, aged eleven, hoped to be a motor mechanic and engineer, when she grew up, shouted back to her Father. "Dad, I think that you will have to use the Land Rover to pull Harvey out of that soft mud. If you like, I will stay behind and help you." Dad shouted back, "That is a very good idea Jane. There is no-one else here on a Sunday to help me."

So Jane changed into her jeans and over-alls. Dad and Jane tied large ropes around Harvey the Bull. The ropes had to go right underneath the bull's stomach. Jane suggested that they use two of the horse's belly-bands to go around the Bull standing in the Duck-pond. (These bands are strong thick leather straps which go underneath and around a horse's belly when the horse is pulling a cart.)

They attached ropes to the bellybands, and Dad got inside the Land Rover. They gently drove the Land-rover a little at a time, because they did not want to hurt the heavy Bull. All at once, the Bull began to kick, and jump about in the pool, and he came rushing and splashing, out of his own accord. They had succeeded in about twenty minutes. The Bull was very cold, but he was free at last. He ran around the field, as if he were a racing horse, warming himself up. He was bellowing loudly.

Dad said, "Jane, thank you for your help this morning. That was a splendid idea to use the horse's harness to put around the Bull. A friend in need is a friend indeed." Jane smiled, and she said thoughtfully, "Jesus would have made a good farmer, he knew that some things on a farm must be done quickly, even on a Sunday. He must have seen many an animal being pulled out of a hole."

Sunday is a good day for saving an animal's life. The better the day, the better the deed. When you come to think about it, many important workers have no choice, but to work on a Sunday. Hospitals must carry on helping their patients. Power stations which provide our electricity must carry on working. The fire-brigade, and the Police must work on a Sunday. The water pumping station must work on. All farmers work on a Sunday. To produce Monday morning's newspaper means that some people have to work on the Sunday beforehand.

Jesus once healed a man on the Sabbath day. The poor sick man had dropsy, a disease which makes people's bodies swell with fluid in parts. (Their legs or arms). Jesus healed the man instantly, and sent him away, healthy and happy. Jesus considered himself to be a helper to other people. Helpful people are useful people to have around.

Prayer:

> Lord God, our dearest friend,
> We thank you for Sunday, a day for worship,
> and a day for recreation.
> We pray for all those people,
> whose life's duties mean that they must work on a Sunday.
> Bless them and give them your peace.   Amen.

Hymn:

We thank you Lord, for all we eat, from farmers' fields. (C&P.2. 136)

Teachers' Note: (1) Sunday is good for worship and going to church. (2) Sunday is also good for recreation. (Doing something different to make fresh energy for the next week.) (3) Sunday is a good day for being helpful. Jane was a clear thinker, as well as being a helpful person.

(c) Simon the Helper

Week 9   Helpers

Simon happened to be standing in a crowd in the old city of Jerusalem. He was not a native of the city. He had been born in Cyrene in Libya in North Africa. He was in Jerusalem on business. The Roman soldiers were coming down the street, apparently leading three criminals to a hill outside the city walls, where they would be put to death. Two of the criminals were thieves. The other one was carrying a wooden notice around his neck. On the notice, the words read, "Jesus of Nazareth, King of the Jews."

Simon thought that the third condemned man looked different from the others. He wore a crown of thorns on his head. He had obviously been whipped by the soldiers. His back was bleeding. He was carrying the cross-beam of a wooden cross on his shoulders. The wooden plank of wood was so heavy that the third prisoner fell under its weight. The rough soldiers lifted the bleeding man, Jesus, back to his feet again.

A Centurion in command of the soldiers, looked at the watching people standing alongside the narrow road. He noticed that Simon of Cyrene was a well-built man. He had strong muscles. The Roman Centurion ordered Simon to help the prisoner. Simon lifted the heavy cross-beam, and carried it for Jesus, all the way through the streets, and out through the city gates. Up the hill called "Calvary" he went. Simon had a good steady character, and he later became a Christian.

The prisoners and the soldiers walked along beside him. Soon the Roman soldiers had reached the top of the small hill. On the ground, the Roman Soldiers nailed the prisoners to the three crosses, and lifted them up. The wooden crosses fitted into holes made in the ground. Simon, walked away from the sad scene. He thought to himself, "At least, I have been some help to that condemned man, Jesus. I have helped him to carry his heavy cross today. He looked utterly exhausted, as if he had missed his sleep in prison for several nights." Truly, Simon of Cyrene that day had been a genuine helper to Jesus in his hour of need.

Children also may be helpers to people in need. It is always good to tell your parents when you are helping grown up people, so that your parents know where you are at the same time.

One Summer evening, Bobby and Alex happened to look through the railings into their school playing fields. They saw their lady P.E. teacher, who always took their class for sports lessons. She was alone, walking up and down, around the school field with her head down. Bobby shouted through the railings. "Please, Miss. Johnson, may we help you?"

She shouted back through the railings, "Yes, Please! I could do with your help. I always wear a silver cross on a chain around my neck at school. I bought it when I was on holiday on the Island of Iona in Scotland. I value it very much. When I reached home this afternoon, I found that I had lost it. It must have fallen off somewhere."

Alex said, "May we go back home and get our dog, Ben? He is a big Labrador dog, but he is very intelligent. He is always finding things. He carries them back home in his mouth." Away the boys ran, and soon they had brought back Ben. They allowed Ben off his lead, because he was inside the school railings. "Go find it," the boys said to Ben.

He was off like a shot, and he started running down the field. Round and round he travelled, smelling and sniffing all the time. His tail was wagging, because he loved searching for lost articles. The two boys urged him on! "Find it boy." Then all at once he stopped, and ran towards the side of the football field. Searching in the long grass, where spectators usually stood. Then his tail wagged furiously. He was carrying something back in his mouth.

Miss Johnson could not believe her eyes. Ben carried a chain and silver cross ever so carefully in his mouth. Alex patted Ben on the head, and gave the chain and cross back to the P.E. Teacher. Bobby noticed that Miss. Johnson had big tears running down her cheeks. "Why are you crying?" Bobby asked her. Miss. Johnson smiled through her tears, and said to the boys, "I am crying for joy! Thank you, boys, you all have been so helpful!"

Bobby and Alex, were very helpful to Miss. Johnson, the P.E. Teacher. They found her silver chain and cross. No wonder they loved Ben, their clever dog! We all may be helpful in some way, to someone, even though we may not have a Labrador dog.

Prayer:

> Heavenly Father, teach us to be helpful
> when we can, to someone else.
> We thank you for the manner in which
> Simon of Cyrene carried the heavy cross for Jesus.
> Make us to be a friend in need.
> Through Jesus Christ our Lord.   Amen.

Hymn:

Bind us together Lord. (JP. 17)

Teachers' Note: (1) Simon of Cyrene was not ashamed to carry the cross-beam for Jesus. (2) Alex and Bobby in being helpful to their P.E. Teacher, found out that people appreciate helpful children. (3) We all can help someone somewhere, as long as our parents know just where we are. Teachers' reference for Simon of Cyrene. Matthew Ch. 27 verse 32. and Mark Ch. 15 verse 21.

(a) Abou Ben Adhem's Dream

Week 10   Poetry

Leigh Hunt was a Poet who was born in the year 1784. He died in 1859. He wrote various poems, but there is one poem, which most people love to read. The poem was written about a good man, who was an Arab. His name was Abou Ben Adhem.

One night, Ben Adhem went to sleep in peace as usual, when he had a dream. He dreamt that an Angel appeared in the room. The moon was shining through the window. The Angel was writing in a Book of Gold. The quietness of the dark night, made Ben Adhem feel very bold. He spoke out to the Angel. "What are you writing?" he asked.

The Angel raised his head, and stopped writing for a moment. He answered. "I am writing the names of those who love the Lord."

"Is my name one of the names in your book?" asked Ben Adhem. The Angel looked at his Golden Book, and replied, "Abou Ben Adhem, your name is not here!"

Ben Adhem thought to himself for a little while. Then he said to the Angel, "I ask you, just to write my name in your Golden Book, as one who loves his fellow men." (human beings). The Angel wrote in his book, and then vanished. The very next night, the Angel came again to the room, surrounded by a light, that was so bright that it awoke Ben Adhem from sleep.

The Angel showed Ben Adhem the Golden Book, in which were written the names of those who had been blessed by the love of God. To Ben Adhem's surprise, his own name, "Abou Ben Adhem" was first on the page of God's Golden Book. Then, the Angel vanished from sight. Ben Adhem was very happy, and slept in peace. He now understood that anyone who loves his fellow human being, also loves God.

Leigh Hunt, the Poet, wanted to teach us that if we say that we love God, then we must also be kind to other people. Abou Ben Adhem was a good example to all of us. Jesus once said to his disciples, "I was naked and you clothed me. I was hungry and you gave me food. I was in prison and you visited me."

The good people who heard, asked Jesus, "When did we ever clothe you, or feed you, or visit you in prison?" Jesus replied, "Whenever you do such good deeds to the least of these my brothers, you do it unto me." Jesus meant that when we help someone else, we are truly serving God.

Prayer:

> Lord our Heavenly Father,
> we thank you for songs, hymns, and for poetry.
> Teach us that to love God,
> we must be kind to other people.
> Show us that in serving other people,
> we are also serving Jesus Christ our Lord.   Amen.

Hymn;

> When I needed a neighbour, were you there? (C&P.1. 65), (JP. 275)

Teachers' Note: (1) Abou Ben Adhem was one of those good people, whom we often meet. They do not so much talk about their faith, as they act it out in daily life. (2) To serve others, is to serve Jesus Christ. Ref: (Matthew Chap. 25 verses 35-40. (3) Faith is much more than good words. Children may write poetry.

(b) Caedmon Singer and Poet   *Week 10   Poetry*

If you ever go to Whitby, you must try to visit Whitby Abbey. The original Abbey stands in ruins, but there is a very old Church which you may visit. To reach the church, you will need to climb many old stone steps, overlooking the harbour. You will find old fashioned pews, in the church, which are still used today. The original Abbey was once under the care of a woman who was known as the Abbess Hilda. She was in charge of the Monks and Nuns who used to live there.

In the grounds of the Abbey, there worked a cowman, by the name of Caedmon. He cleaned out the cow-sheds, and milked the cows each day. The milk was needed to feed the monks and nuns who lived at the Abbey. Caedmon was glad that he had such a secure job. It is surprising to learn that Caedmon was not a monk. Indeed, he could neither read nor write. He had a hard life, but Caedmon was a deeply contented kind of person.

In those days there were no cinemas or theatres to attend. There was no television. Country people used to entertain themselves by holding local Concerts. The farm workers would perform, or sing or play a musical instrument.

Since, Caedmon could do neither, he slipped away to lie on the straw in his cow-shed. He fell asleep.

As Caedmon lay sleeping, he heard a voice calling his name. "Caedmon, will you sing for me?" Caedmon realised that the voice was the voice of God calling him. Caedmon replied, "Lord I cannot sing." God answered Caedmon. He said, "Caedmon, I will help you to sing. You could sing of God's beautiful world, just like David, who wrote many of the psalms in the Bible. You could sing Praises unto the Lord, and glorify God, who made the seas, stars, and the whole world."

Caedmon realised that God was going to use him as a Christian singer. He began to practise using his voice in song. At first, his voice was weak and not very tune-ful, but as time went by, his voice became stronger, rich, and his tones became pure. He kept exercising his breathing, and learned to project his voice, either loudly, or very quietly. The Abbess Hilda heard many reports of Caedmon's ability to sing. Hilda realised that Caedmon had received a gift from God. He became God's Sweet Singer.

The Monks taught Caedmon the stories from the Bible. Caedmon had another gift, he discovered that he could easily write poetry. He began to turn the Bible stories into verses. The monks used to eat their meals together at a long table, in a large dining room, known as the "Refectory". One day when they were all gathered together after dinner, Caedmon happened to be passing through the long room. To everyone's surprise, Caedmon the cowman stood up on a wooden bench, and he began to sing. The refectory was crowded that day, and the monks listened intently to the cowman singing. His beautiful voice was stronger and sweeter than they had ever heard anyone sing before. His eyes glistened as he sang of the goodness of God in the world. The monks could see that he was singing from his heart. Everyone realised that Caedmon had received a special gift from God. He was God's sweet singer.

Later he set more Bible stories to music. His beautiful singing voice led many to believe in the Lord Jesus, and to join the Church. If you ever go to visit the Abbey at Whitby, you must look for the Caedmon stone. On the stone is carved the words, beginning, "Praise we loudly the Lord of Heaven."

Children may also learn to write poetry. They could even write hymns, if they tried hard enough. What is more, children are very good at singing the praises of God, either as a solo, or as a choir.

Prayer:

Heavenly Father, we thank you for Christian praise.
We thank you for Caedmon, the Singer of Whitby Abbey.
Teach us that we may pray as we sing.
Help us all to use our talents.

Forgive us our faults and our failings.
Bless and forgive us, for Jesus Christ's sake.   Amen.

Hymn:

God is love, His the care. (C&P.1. 36)

Teachers' Note: (1) Caedmon had a very humble beginning, he was only a cowman, and a gardener. (2) God needed Caedmon's voice, so that he might sing to God's glory. (3) The ordinary people around Whitby fishing village, and the Monks at the Abbey, and St. Hilda herself, all were blessed by Caedmon's poetry.

(c) The Shortest Psalm   *Week 10   Poetry*

The children at the school all loved Miss. Briggs, because she could be such fun. It is true that she was very strict about everyone working hard in Class, but on the other hand, she could kick a football on the school field. Miss. Briggs came to school one day wearing an eye patch across one eye, just like a Pirate. She was not joking this time, because the wind had blown dust into her eye. The dust particles hurt her very much.

In the Assembly she had been talking about the Psalms, which are old Jewish songs and poems. They are found written in the Bible. She said that long ago, children at school used to learn the Psalms off by heart. Then, she asked the Children to learn by heart, Psalm 119. Miss. Briggs said that it was the shortest Psalm in the Bible. She said that she would give a prize of a bar of chocolate, to any of the children who could say Psalm 119 off by heart, in any version, at the Assembly, the following morning.

After school, many of the children looked up Psalm 119 in the Bible, only to find that it had 176 verses in it. None of the children felt that they were able to learn off by heart, so many verses at once. So they did not learn anything. Now, there was one girl, named Sally Bright, who when she grew up, became a lady detective in the local Police Station. She was a highly intelligent girl, and always asking questions about everything. She looked up her big Family Bible at home, and she also found that Psalm 119 had 176 verses in it. She knew that nobody could learn off so many verses in one evening. She wondered if Miss. Briggs was playing one of her little tricks on the children.

The more Sally Bright thought about the matter, the more she felt that there was another explanation. Could Miss. Briggs have made a mistake in the referring to the number of the Psalm? She remembered that Miss Briggs had a sore eye. Sally Bright tried to remember what Miss. Briggs had said. She remembered that Miss. Briggs had mentioned that it was the shortest Psalm in the Bible.

Sally thought to herself, that was the answer to the problem! There were 150 Psalms in the Book of Psalms, and all Sally had to do was to find the Psalm with the shortest number of verses. Sally Bright soon found that the shortest Psalm was Psalm 117. That Psalm was quite near Psalm 119. It had only two verses. Miss. Briggs having had a sore eye that morning, had not read the number correctly. Before Sally Bright slept, she learned off by heart, these words.

Psalm 117
O praise the Lord, all you nations.
Praise him all you peoples.
For his merciful kindness is great toward us:
and the truth of the Lord endures for ever.
Praise you the Lord!

When Sally Bright woke up next morning, she rhymed off Psalm 117. Before she ate her breakfast, Sally rhymed off Psalm 117. Before she cleaned her teeth, Sally rhymed off Psalm 117. So, she had the Psalm off by heart, when Assembly time came round.

When Miss. Briggs asked whether anyone had bothered to learn off the Psalm, Sally Bright raised her hand. She came out to the front of the Assembly, and repeated the Psalm 117 perfectly. All the children clapped. Miss. Briggs smiled at her, and gave her the big bar of chocolate as a prize. Sally said nothing about Miss. Briggs' mistake.

Miss. Briggs suggested that the children could have another try. The Question was, *"What was the shortest verse in the whole Bible?* If you find out the answer,"* Miss. Briggs smiled again and said, "if you like, you can bring me a bar of chocolate!" Some of the children 'phoned up the Vicar, and he told them the answer. Next morning, the children brought her more than one hundred bars of chocolate. They all knew the answer.

Sally Bright somehow felt, that Miss. Briggs had got the best of the bargain, even though Miss. Briggs later shared out the bars of chocolate among the Assembly children. Everyone was happy!

DO YOU KNOW THE ANSWER, CHILDREN?

Teacher Note: (The shortest verse in the Bible is "Jesus wept". (St. John, Chapter 11 verse 35.)

Prayer:

Lord God, our Heavenly Father,
We are grateful for all our Teachers in School.
Bless them and reward them for the work,
which they put into our Education.
May we as children become good learners.   Amen.

Hymn:

(C&P.1. 56), (JP. 243)

Teachers' Note: (1) There is a note of humour in this story. Miss. Briggs may have been wiser than everyone thought she was. Was she testing the children? (2) In every class there are one or two Sally Bright's (highly intelligent children ahead of the others). (3) Many of the Psalms are beautiful poetry, (eg; Psalm 23) and they are really worth knowing. ("Ye" meant "you" in the 1611 version of the Bible) Teachers may initiate other questions. eg. How many books are in the Bible? How many Gospels are there? etc.

(a) **Snowball the Rabbit**   *Week 11   Towards Christmas*

Lucy dearly loved her mother. Since it was coming near Christmas, she wondered what present to buy for her Mum. She had looked in the shop windows at boxes of handkerchiefs, jewellery, scarves, talcum powder, and such things as slippers, and perfume, but she really could not make up her mind.

The most important present that Lucy hoped for herself, was that she would get a a rabbit and a hutch. Lucy hated zoos, where animals were caged up behind bars. However, she thought to herself, that if she had a rabbit, that she would let it play about in the garden, when she came home from school every afternoon. She thought that would be different from an animal being behind bars in a zoo. Lucy was very disappointed when her mother said that she could not have a rabbit for her Christmas present. Her Dad agreed, saying that keeping rabbits was too much work.

Lucy was rather a selfish little girl, who liked to get her own way. She began to think and to plan in her mind, just how to get her own way. Lucy thought that if she opened her money box, she would have enough money to buy a white New Zealand rabbit. She liked that breed, because white New Zealand rabbits were big rabbits with soft white fluffy fur.

Then Lucy had an idea. She thought to herself, "If I bought a rabbit as a present, for my Dad, then I could take care of the rabbit for him, when he was at work." This way, she thought that although she was supposed to be giving the rabbit to her father, she would really be buying it for herself. He would be away every day at his work anyway. Two weeks before Christmas, Lucy opened her money box, without telling her Mum, and took out enough money to buy a white New Zealand rabbit, and also a rabbit hutch.

When the pet shop van drove up to her front door, Lucy was at school. Her mother was told by the van driver that the rabbit and hutch were already paid for, and that he had been instructed to deliver them to Mr. Albert Brown, her husband.

Mrs. Brown had no other choice, but to take delivery of one hutch and one white New Zealand rabbit.

Lucy came home from school, and she began to play with the rabbit in the back garden. When her Dad came home, she said, much to her mother's surprise, "Dad, I have bought you a present for Christmas." She smiled sweetly at her father. Mum did not want to be angry about her little girl buying her Dad a Christmas present. So that is how selfish Lucy got her own way. They called the rabbit "Snowball" because he was a pure white colour. Lucy bought her Mum a bottle of perfume, to persuade her that all was well.

However, from the moment Snowball arrived, there was trouble. First, the rabbit escaped into the neighbour's garden next door, and he ate the expensive window box flowers belonging to the lady. Then, he happened to get into Lucy's house. He chewed the electric flex behind the television, and that caused Mr. Brown's television to fuse, and go on fire. Next, the rabbit chewed a hole in Mrs. Brown's best "going out dress", which had blown off the washing line.

The following day, Snowball became sick, and had to be taken to the Vet. He was kept over-night in the Vet's dispensary. This was very expensive, and Dad had to pay the Vet. Snowball escaped a second time, and was lost for two days. Then the police phoned to say that they had found the rabbit, and that they given it to the "R.S.P.C.A.". That was enough for Lucy's Dad. He 'phoned the "R.S.P.C.A." and told them to keep Snowball. He suggested that they gave it away to someone who really liked rabbits.

Lucy knew that she herself was the cause of all the trouble. She too had become tired of the rabbit by this time. She told her Mum and Dad that she had only bought Snowball, because she had wanted the Rabbit for herself. Now she did not want it anymore, because keeping even one rabbit, was a lot of work. Lucy realised that she had been greedy and selfish, while all the time she had pretended to be giving her Dad a Christmas present. Lucy was sorry that she had been so greedy and selfish. She knew in herself that one must never give a present for the wrong reasons.

Prayer:

> Good Heavenly Father, we thank you
> for your generosity to people everywhere.
> You have given us a wonderful world to enjoy.
> You have given to each of us the gift of life.
> Most of all you loved us, and gave us Jesus
> to be our Saviour and our example.　　Amen.

Hymn:

> All the animals I have ever seen. (C&P.2. 80)

Teachers Note: (1) The children may like to discuss why we give presents. Just like Lucy, we may give presents to others for selfish reasons. (2) There is a genuine joy which comes to us, in giving to others. (3) Christmas is a lovely time to give presents because God gave us the little baby, Jesus, who was born in a stable.

(b) The Little Pup   *Week 11   Looking towards Christmas*

The Millar family all wanted a little pup for Christmas. They lived in London, where they did not see many animals. John, Helen, Peter, Debbie, and baby Mark, all lived together with their Mum and Dad in a small house. A week before Christmas, they all went down to the pet shop. They looked at the cuddly puppies for sale. They liked the sheep dog puppies best of all. There were seven of them to chose from, so they chose a little brown and white puppy.

The Millar family paid the pet shop owner for the tiny puppy, and asked him to put a small collar around his neck. On Christmas Eve, the family called back again at the shop, to collect their little dog. They had also bought a small plastic dog basket, which was much too large for the little animal. Previously, the little puppy had been kept warm, sleeping beside his six tiny brothers and sisters. Lovingly, they put an old blanket into the plastic basket to keep the puppy cosy and warm. Soon, they all arrived home.

They awoke early on Christmas morning. John, Helen, Peter, and Debbie and Mum with Dad, carrying baby Mark, all went into the living room to see their new arrival. The pup looked so small in the dog basket. How happy the Millar family was that day. They named their dog "Tiny." They treated him as if he were a new toy.

The days, weeks, and months passed by quickly. The little sheep dog seemed to grow very fast. The pup seemed to eat enormous meals. His legs and paws grew very big. He was growing very large indeed, and his hair became very long, and covered the dog's face so much, that one could not see the dog's eyes. They did not know at that time, but they had bought, not just a a collie sheep dog, but what turned out to be an Old English Sheepdog.

The dog became so large, that no-one could sit on the settee, if the dog was lying on it first. He became far too large for the living room of their little house. Although his name was "Tiny" the dog grew into a very large animal. Indeed, the Millar family became tired of having such a big dog in their small house. They wondered just what they could do to get rid of their pet. Mr. Millar took the dog in his car, and raced fifty miles up the Motorway, and then he turned off into a quiet country lane. He opened the car door, and pushed Tiny out.

He drove away back home again to London leaving Tiny to wander about in the strange countryside.

Tiny had become one more of the many animals that people buy at Christmas time, and then later the animals are dumped somewhere, when they become a nuisance. Poor Tiny wandered away from the Motorway into a nearby farm. He was lost. The kind farmer had other dogs, but when he saw just how large, and how young Tiny was, he liked the dog very much indeed. He 'phoned the police station, and informed the desk Sergeant that he had found a stray dog, and that he would love to keep it. The Farmer kept Tiny as a work dog. Tiny had his own kennel along with the other farm dogs.

Sad to say, the Millar family never came back to look for their pet dog. They were glad to get rid of Tiny. The farmer gave the dog a new name. He named him, "Bonnie." (which means "beautiful"). The big sheep dog felt happy, now that he was a work dog and not a toy. He loved to gently bring the sheep and their lambs together, down the hill-side, when ordered by a whistle from the farmer.

Not all stray dogs end up in a such a happy situation. Children and adults must not treat dogs as if they were Christmas toys, which can be thrown away, when people get tired of keeping them. Animals have rights as well as human beings. Do you agree?

Prayer:

> O Lord and Father of Jesus Christ,
> We thank you for Christmas time,
> and for the opportunity of receiving presents.
> Teach us to be kind to animals.
> We thank you for the faithfulness of our pets.   Amen.

Hymn:

> The King of love my shepherd is. (C&P.1. 54), (JP. 241)

Teachers' Note: (1) The Millar family were very sincere in wanting a little puppy at Christmas. However, puppies all have to grow up. (2) Not all dogs are similar, in size, or in temperament. One may buy what turns out to be an unsuitable dog. (3) This would be a good place to point out that animals have rights, just as human beings have rights. (Such as kindness and discipline).

(c) The Wise Men   *Week 11   Towards Christmas*

Long ago, in one of the Eastern countries, there were Wise men. They had spent their lives studying the shining stars in the sky. One evening, a specially bright star appeared. They believed that it was a new star. They also believed that a new star foretold the birth of a new King upon the Earth.

The Wise Men decided to visit the newly born baby, and give presents to him. They brought three different presents. Perhaps, because there were three presents, that is why people assumed that there were "three" Wise men. The Bible says only that "Wise Men came from the East" There may have been "three" Wise Men, or even four or more.

They carried gold, frankincense and myrrh as presents for the new baby. The Wise men set off on their camels, on their long journey to the land of Palestine, following the star, which moved like a shining jewel in the dark sky towards Jerusalem. They had no other means of knowing the direction, but to follow the moving star each night.

At last, they reached the King's palace, in Jerusalem. The Wise Men paid a visit to King Herod. They asked where the baby Prince was to be born. Herod was afraid, because he was a bad King. He did not want a new prince to be born in his Kingdom. Herod was afraid that the people might obey the new-born King, instead of him. He told the Wise men that when they found the new baby King, that they should tell him where the baby lived. Herod did not tell the Wise Men but he really wanted to kill the new baby, as soon as possible.

King Herod asked the Jewish Priests and Scribes where the Messiah was to be born. The Priests informed Herod that Micah, the Old Testament prophet, had foretold in his book that the Messiah would be born in Bethlehem in Judaea. That night the Star appeared again. The Wise Men followed it to the village of Bethlehem. When they came to the stable where Mary and the baby Jesus were, the Star seemed to come to a halt. It remained shining down overhead. The Wise Men knew that they had arrived at the right place.

The Wise Men presented their gifts to the baby Jesus, Gold, Frankincense, and Myrrh. They bowed and worshiped Jesus. Mary loved and cuddled her precious little baby She kept like a treasure, all these happenings in her mind. The Wise Men bowed to the Holy Child Jesus once more, and then left on their return journey. God had warned them in a dream, that they should not go back to King Herod. They returned to their own country by another way.

The Angel of the Lord appeared to Joseph, Mary's husband, in a dream. He warned Joseph that King Herod would try to kill the baby Jesus. He said, "Arise, take the young child, and Mary his mother, and escape into Egypt." So that night, Joseph and Mary escaped with the baby Jesus, and journeyed into Egypt. They remained there until King Herod was dead. After King Herod's death, the Holy Family returned to live in Nazareth. For this reason, Jesus was later known as a "Nazarene."

Prayer:

> Most gracious Heavenly Father,
> we thank you for the story of the Wise Men.
> Lord of all wisdom, teach us that Christmas
> is about giving to others.
> Show us, that it more blessed to give,
> than to receive. Through Jesus Christ our Lord.   Amen.

Hymn:

> Riding out across the desert. (C&P.2. 124)

Teachers' Note: (1) Children think in terms of presents which they hope to receive at Christmas. This is natural! This Lesson poses the question, "What can children give, and to whom?" (2) Most people assume that because there were three presents given to Jesus, that there were also three givers. This is not necessarily so. (3) The Wise men were (a) Seekers. (b) Finders. (c) Givers.

Additional Teachers' Note: *Frankinscense* was a white sweet smelling gum, which has a fragrant smell when it is burned. It was mixed with oil when a Priest was being dedicated. (Exodus 30 verse 34.) *Myrrh* was used to anoint the Priests. (Exodus 30 verse 23), and also to anoint the dead, before they were buried. Gold was the precious metal that made the kings rich men.

References: See Micah 5.v.2. Matthew Chap. 2 verses -23.

(a) Tammy's Hair
Week 12   Christmas

Tammy was aged ten. She had been very ill, and had nearly died. She had to stay in hospital for quite a long time. The Doctors had given her treatment which had helped her serious illness, but it had caused all her hair to fall out. Tammy felt very embarrassed, because she felt so odd-looking without her beautiful auburn hair. She thought to herself. "I wonder what the children back at the primary school would think of me now."

It would soon be Christmas. The other children in the hospital ward were talking about the presents they would be getting on Christmas day. Some wanted personal stereos. Others wanted Barbie dolls or Action men. Some even were hoping for a computer. Those who were going home talked about getting mountain bikes. Tammy wanted only one present for her Christmas. She wanted her hair to grow again, for Christmas day. Away back in August, the Doctors had said that her treatment and therapy had been completed, but that she would have to stay in hospital until December.

Tammy's teacher came to see her in hospital in August. Tammy told her that her treatment had been completed, but that she had to stay in hospital under observation for several more months. She whispered to her Teacher that she had been praying that her hair would grow again for Christmas. When her Teacher went home, she also began to pray every day, that Tammy's hair might grow again. When she went to the school Assembly, the following week, she told the children at the Assembly about Tammy, and about her loss of hair caused by the treatment.

The children and the Teacher's decided to pray that Tammy would be made well, and that her hair would grow again for Christmas. They remembered that once she had a beautiful head of long auburn coloured hair. The children were wise and kind enough to know that they must never laugh at anyone in the school, who had lost their hair through illness. Sick children were God's special children.

One day in October, little hairs began to appear on Tammy's head. The hair was fluffy, just like as if she had been a baby. Tammy used to go into the bathroom, to look into the mirror to look at the top of her head. Then in the month of November, her hair became much longer, and the Nurse said with a smile on her face, "O Tammy, I do believe that hair is growing on your scalp again." She was right!

Each week, of November, the hair continued to grow. Tammy was delighted. Each night, she said her prayers, thanking God, that she was getting well again. By the third week in December, her hair was quite long. The Doctor said to Tammy, "Tammy, I think you should have the hair-dresser to straighten up the edges of your hair. They will not take much hair off, but you might be allowed home on Christmas week. You want your hair to look nice." Again, Tammy said her prayer of thanks to God.

When Christmas week arrived, Tammy's Parents had come to visit her. The Senior Doctor hurried up the Ward, and said to Tammy's Parents, "Tammy is well enough to go home now." Even though the three adult people were beside her, she closed her eyes, and said a little prayer. "Thank you Lord, for making my hair come back again, and thank you for the Doctors and Nurses. Most of all, thank you Lord, for getting me home again in time for Jesus' birthday."

When the news reached the school, the Teachers and the Children at the Assembly, also said a little prayer of thanksgiving. As she combed her hair, Tammy felt that she had received the best Christmas present in the whole world.

Prayer:

O Lord and Healer of us all,
Today, we pray for all sick children.
We thank you for Doctors, and Nurses.

Especially at Christmas time,
Bless the children and heal their bodies.   Amen.

Hymn;

The Virgin Mary had a baby boy. (C&P.2. 121), (JP. 251)

Teachers' Note: (1) In our happiness, we must never forget that there are many sick children in the world. (2) It is good to remember that God cares for sick children. (3) Our private prayer, joined to the prayers of others, has a healing power. We ought to also thank God for the skills of Doctors and Nurses.

(b) A Christmas Carol   *Week 12   Christmas*

Do you ever wonder what events lie behind a hymn? Here is a true story telling us what events lay behind the lovely Christmas hymn, which we usually sing at Christmas time.

"O little town of Bethlehem
How still we see thee lie."

The Rev. Phillip Brooks was an American Episcopal minister, who lived during the 19th century. He had a famous church in Philadelphia. Phillip Brooks was a very tall man, who loved to speak to children. It is said that he could sing 200 hymns from memory.

He went against all the rules of public speaking when preaching in the pulpit. He could speak at a very rapid rate, as though he were an auctioneer selling goods. However, his pronunciation must have been very clear, for people to understand what he was saying. People loved to hear this famous preacher preaching from his pulpit. He never married. He later became a Bishop. More than anything else, he loved to talk to children. They were fascinated by his children's talks.

Phillip Brooks had an opportunity to visit Bethlehem, the village where Jesus was born as a baby. That visit occurred during December 1865, and it left a deep impression on his mind. He thought to himself, "How wonderful! I have actually been to the place where Jesus was born." He arrived back home to his beautiful church in the city of Philadelphia, and kept what he had seen in Bethlehem hidden in his mind. He had really enjoyed his visit.

Three years passed, and Christmas time came round once more. Brooks had just finished preparing his Sermon for Christmas Day. He felt a strange urge to write a poem about Bethlehem. He quickly wrote down the words of a poem for the Sunday School to sing at Christmas. Here are the first lines.

"O little Town of Bethlehem,
 How still we see thee lie,
Above thy deep and dreamless sleep,
The silent stars go by.
Yet in thy dark street shineth
The everlasting light;
The joys and fears of all the years
Are met in thee tonight.

The Leader of the Sunday School was also the church Organist. His name was Lewis Redner, and at that moment, he was practising playing hymns on an organ in the adjoining room. Phillip Brooks gave the completed written poem to his friend, Lewis, and asked him to compose a tune for it, so that the children could sing it over the Christmas period.

Lewis Redner went home, and tried for days to compose a tune, but he just could not do it. Lewis went to bed early on Christmas eve, and fell asleep. Just about mid-night, he woke up, and he took up a pen, because he could hear a new tune in his mind. He quickly wrote the notes on a piece of paper lying beside his bed, and then he went back to sleep again. The tune seemed to fit the words perfectly. It was as if the notes had come from the Lord himself.

Lewis Redner, the Leader of the Sunday School later taught the new Carol to the children, and they sang it together as a children's choir, on Christmas Day 1868 in Church. The Rev. Phillip Brooks and his congregation loved the Carol, from the moment they heard it. Ever since, children and adults having been singing the Carol all over the world.

Phillip Brooks died in the year 1893. Maybe, Phillip Brooks did more good by writing this one carol, than by all his wonderful preaching, which now is forgotten. His Carol lives on in the hearts of many people.

Do you think that you could write a Christmas poem this week, all by yourself?

Prayer:

Lord of Christmas time,
We thank you for the joy of singing Carols.
We pray that all children everywhere,
may have a truly happy Christmas.
We pray for poor and hungry people overseas.   Amen.

Hymn:

O Little town of Bethlehem, (J.P. 182)
or, I want to see your baby boy. (C&P.2. 117)

Teachers' Note: (1) This would be a good opportunity for children to attempt to write a Christmas poem. (2) How many carols do the children know? Which is their favourite carol. Which carol is their parent's favourite? (3) Carols all carry a message, and an atmosphere of their own. Illustrate this from the Carol "In the bleak mid-Winter."

(c) Christmas Questions
Week 12   Christmas

Let us have a Christmas Quiz today, instead of a story. No-one is allowed to shout out answers in the Assembly. We could have two or three teams to take part. The game is to answer the **twenty questions** *correctly. Each time the question is put, only one member of the Team will be given an opportunity to answer, for an award of* **TWO** *Points. If that person cannot answer, then the anyone in the Team may answer for an award of* **ONE** *Point. A member of the Staff may be appointed Question Master/Mistress. A second person could act as Recorder, and keep an account of the points gained by each team. (The included Scripture References are for the convenience of the Teacher).*

Questions

1. What was the name of the town where Jesus was born? *(Bethlehem)*

2. What was the name of the village where Jesus was brought up as a little boy. *(Nazareth)*

3. What was the name of Mary's husband? *(Joseph)*

4. What was the name of Mary's cousin, who was also expecting a baby at that time? *(Elizabeth)*
(Luke Chapter 1, verse 36)

5. What was the name of Elizabeth's little baby?
(John) (later, "the Baptist")

6. What was the name of the King, to whom the Wise Men paid a visit, as they followed the Star? *(Herod)*

7. How many Wise Men were there?
(No number is given. Scripture just states that "Wise Men came from the East." We do know that they brought three gifts.) There is a later story/tradition that the visitors were three Eastern Kings. (Points here for those who knew that "three" was not in the scriptural story.)

8. What were the three gifts which the
    Wise men brought to Jesus?   *(Gold, frankincense, and myrrh)*

9. What was the name of the Angel who appeared
    to Mary, the mother of Jesus?   *(Angel Gabriel)*
    (See Luke Chapter 1, verse 26)

10. Another company of men came to visit the
    baby Jesus. Who were they?   *(The Shepherds)*
    (See Luke Chapter 2, verses 8-20)

11. Name any four things in life associated with
    Christmas beginning with the letter "C."
    (Possibly; crib, carols, candles,
    cards, cake, crackers, or Christ)

12. What was Santa Claus' original name?   *(St. Nicholas)*

13. Why do we have special lights at Christmas time?
    eg. Lights on a Christmas Tree)   *(Because we celebrate that*
    Jesus was, "the Light of the world",
    and/or Christmas is held at the
    darkest part of the year.
    (Eg. shortest daylight)

14. Name a Christmas Carol beginning with the letter, "A".
    (Away in a manger)

15. Name a Carol beginning with the letter "S"   *(Silent Night)*

16. Name the day after "Christmas day"?   *(Boxing Day)*

17. Name five things or people beginning with the
    letter "S" connected with Christmas?
    (Star, shepherds, sheep, stable, Saviour,
    Simeon, or just words such as stocking,
    Santa, sleigh. Simeon was the old man who
    lived in Jerusalem, who in the Temple
    courtyard took Jesus as a baby in his arms,
    and gave God thanks for his birth.) See St.
    Luke Ch.2, verse 25 -32.

18. Which well known Carol is about something which
    is green and red in colour?   *(The holly and the ivy)*

19. Which carol is about a King who saw a poor man
    gathering firewood on a snowy day?   *(Good King Wenceslas)*

20. Why was Jesus born in a stable?   *(Because there was no*
    room in the Inn)

Prayer:

>Good Lord, bless our school and its Staff.
>We pray for poor children, who must live
>in Local Care Homes at Christmas time.
>We pray for hungry and sick children.
>Bless them all, and may the message
>of Christmas bring them happiness.   Amen.

Hymn:

Hark the herald angels sing. (JP. 69) or, The holly and the ivy. (C&P.2. 119) or, Away in a Manger. (JP. 12)

Teachers' Note: (1) These questions are meant to be fun. At the same time, this is a pleasant way to sum up the teaching of the Christmas theme. (2) This is also an appropriate method of bringing even the most shy of children into participation in the Assembly. (3) When children have answered the questions successfully, the winning Team should be acknowledged and rewarded in some small way.

Spring Term

(a) Martha Thompson's Hymn

This is a story of how a young lady made a new beginning in her life by becoming a Methodist, (a denomination of the Christian Church). Many other people who have made a new start in their lives have become Anglicans, Baptists, Catholics, or Salvationists. God has helped many people in different ways to find peace of mind. Here is the story of Martha Thompson who lived in Lancashire in the 18th. Century.

It was the year 1750. There were no buses in those days. A girl of 19 years of age, waited at the Old Dog Inn in Preston, for the carrier's cart, to take her to Bolton, and then on to Manchester. Martha's mother had died. Her father had re-married, and she did not get on very well with her step-mother. Martha wrote to a rich lady in London, who needed a domestic servant in her big house. The lady had lived in Preston some time before she had moved to London. Anyone wanting to get to London in those days, had to travel a three days journey by stage coach.

Martha liked her job in the big house, because she was a good worker. One day as she was going towards the city, and as she passed through a district known as "Moorfields," she came across a great crowd of people listening to a little man in the dress of an Anglican clergyman. He wore a black gown and white bands. He spoke with an educated voice. Martha listen to the preacher, who often preached to the people in the streets or on the village greens of Britain. Martha was fascinated by what he had to say.

When she told her Mistress about hearing the street preacher, her Mistress was shocked. She said, "Why, Martha, that was John Wesley whom you have been listening to. You must never go there again. Those Methodists are fanatics." Martha did not listen to her Mistress. She went back again to hear Mr. Wesley preaching. He invited people to give their lives to Jesus, and to become Christians.

Martha closed her eyes, and she said a little prayer. She gave her life to Jesus Christ. The last hymn at the open air meeting was a hymn by Isaac Watts, "The Lord Jehovah reigns." (No. 59 in the present Methodist hymn Book). It was sung to the tune, "Darwall's". Martha had never heard such joyful singing before. She rushed home, and told her Mistress and the other servants what had happened to her. The servants complained to their Mistress that Martha Thompson had been singing little bits of "The Lord Jehovah reigns" while she was doing her work. The Master of the House called in two Doctors, who declared that Martha had religious mania. Poor Martha was take by force in a coach, to Bedlam, the London mad-house. Bedlam was full of violent and demented people, who were mentally and physically ill. They were all locked up together. That is how Martha Thompson found herself in a hospital which dealt with mental illness.

The Matron of Bedlam soon noticed that Martha was different from the other patients. She was trusted to work in the institution. One day, she met a Methodist layman who was visiting his sick wife. Martha gave the man a letter for John Wesley. Within a day, Mr. Wesley sent two Doctors to investigate her case. They reported that Martha was not mad, but perfectly normal in her mental health. She was set free immediately. Martha was cared for, clothed and fed at the Methodist headquarters.

Martha now wanted to go home to Preston, in Lancashire. Her life had been changed. She rode behind John Wesley on the back of his horse, and travelled with him as far North as Stafford. From there she travelled by coach to Preston. Martha was sorry that there was no Methodist Society in Preston. She had to walk six miles every Sunday, with the landlady of the Dog and Bull Inn to the nearest Methodist Society. After a few months of hard work, they opened a Methodist Society in a room at the Dog and Bull Inn in Preston. Local Preachers conducted the services.

When, afterwards Mr. Wesley came riding on his horse, to preach at Chorley, some fifteen miles away, Martha paid for the members of the little group to go by Stage Coach, to hear him. As John Wesley preached to the people, the Stage Coach Driver listened intently. So powerful was the teaching that he too decided to become a Christian. Eventually, Martha married a rich button manufacturer from Birmingham. She had many children. One of her grandsons later became Mayor of Preston. Martha never forgot Isaac Watts hymn, "The Lord Jehovah reigns," or the peace of mind brought to her by living her life as a Christian.

Prayer:
>Lord God, our Heavenly Father,
>We thank you for Christians Leaders
>and ordinary people, from all churches,
>who have been a help to needy people.
>We thank you for the life of
>Martha Thompson of Preston,
>who gave her life to Christian Charity. Amen.

Hymn:
>One more step along the world I go. (C&P.1. 47), (JP. 188)

Teachers' Note: (1) Every Church has a history. This is a snippet from Methodist history. (2) Notice that church history is made up of ordinary people, whose lives were changed by God. Can the children name any person whose life was changed? (3) Children may experience an inward change themselves at Confirmation. On the other hand, they may not.

(b) St. Augustine of Hippo   *Week 1   New Beginnings*

In the fourth Century, there was once a family which lived together in the town of Thagaste, in Roman North Africa. Their country bordered on the warm blue Mediterranean Sea. The Father was a City Councillor, named Patritius. He was not a Christian. The mother of the family was named "Monica". She was a very good Christian. Both parents believed deeply in Education. In the year 354 A.D. a little baby was born into the family, whom they called Augustine.

Augustine was a normal boy, and he grew up to be very fond of sport and fun. Sometimes he was disobedient, and rebellious. He himself tells us that once, he joined a group of other boys, and they raided a pear tree. He and his friends climbed the tree, and stripped the pears off every branch. The boys were not really hungry, so they threw the pears to some pigs that were nearby.

Even when Augustine grew up, he did not give up his rebellious ways. However, at the University, he proved himself to be a brilliant student. First, he studied Law, and then Teaching. Augustine when a man, became a seeker after the truth.

After a time, he sailed across the sea to Italy. There were many bad habits in his life, but like many more people, he could not give them up. Augustine met Bishop Ambrose in Italy, and that meeting helped Augustine to begin to search for peace of mind.

One day, Augustine was walking in a quiet part of a garden, when he came across a book on a table. The book was a copy of St. Paul's Epistle to the Romans, (in the Bible). Suddenly, he heard a voice, like the voice of a child. The voice called out, "Take up and read." Augustine began to read the Epistle of Romans. He read that the Apostle Paul had written that they were to behave decently. They were not to be causing riots. They were not to become drunken, or to quarrel, or to be jealous, or to live wrongly. He read that he was to clothe himself with the Lord Jesus. (Romans 13.v. 14). At last, Augustine believed and found peace of mind.

To Augustine, it seemed that God was calling him away from his evil ways to a Christian way of life. So at the age of 38 years, Augustine became a Christian. Augustine's Mother, Monica, was so thankful that her clever son had at last changed for the good. Sad to say, Monica died, soon after, but she was so pleased that she had been permitted to live long enough to see her son's change of life.

Augustine returned to his home-town again, and became a writer of important books for the Church. Some four years passed, and Augustine became a Priest. Four more years passed, and Augustine was consecrated Bishop of Hippo, which is a district in North Africa. Hippo means "horse" in the Greek language. Maybe there was a market for beautiful Arabian horses in that place, or maybe there was a hippodrome there, which is a racecourse for horses. Augustine lived long enough to be a Bishop for thirty four years. He was highly honoured by everyone.

People came and asked his advice. His books such as "The Confessions of St. Augustine," and "The City of God" have been famous for more than a thousand years. It just goes to show that even a boy who joined a gang, and robbed pears from a neighbour's tree, could experience a change of life, and become a true servant of God.

Prayer:

> Our Blessed Heavenly Father,
> We thank you for the story of St. Augustine,
> And his call to the Christian ministry.
> Bless all children, and teach them,
> That God loves them, every one.
> Help us to work hard at school
> that we too might become useful in helping others.   Amen.

Hymn:

> Now thank we all our God. (C&P.1. 38), (JP. 175)

Teachers' Note: (1) (Caution here. Note that it is Augustine of Hippo, we are discussing here, not our own Augustine of Canterbury). Augustine might have been rebellious, but his parents still loved him. (2) Augustine studied hard at school, and University. (3) Augustine was able to help many more people, when he became Bishop of Hippo. We take in knowledge to give it out again. (The Church acknowledged that Monica, his mother, also became known as a "Saint".)

(c) Fall from a Window   *Week 1   New Beginnings*

Paul was a Jew who happened to be a Jewish teacher. His original name was "Saul of Tarsus." Paul means "small," so maybe he was later called "Paul," just because he was rather a small person. Paul hated the very name of Jesus, and also that of his followers who were called "Christians."

One day, on a long journey, he was accompanied by soldiers. They intended to arrest and put into prison, every Christian they could find. As they went down the road to Damascus, there was a flash of light. A voice called out, "Saul, Saul, why are you persecuting me?" Paul asked, "Who are you?" The voice answered, "I am Jesus, whom you are persecuting."

Paul had fallen to the ground, along with the soldiers, when they had seen the flash of light. Paul rose up, stood on his feet, and decided from that day onwards, that he would serve the Lord Jesus. Paul became a Christian. He had made a new beginning in his life.

He was blinded by the flash of light. So they took Paul to the house of a Christian named Ananias, in Straight Street, in Damascus. Ananias proved to be a friend to Paul. Three days later, Paul received back his eyesight. He could see again. Now, Paul became a Christian Preacher, and travelled the Near Eastern countries telling people about Jesus.

After a time, Paul, came to a town called "Troas." Since he was a travelling preacher, he intended to leave the following day. On the Sunday, he "shared bread and wine" with the Christian people. This means that they shared the "Holy Communion" sacrament with his fellow Christians.

Because he knew that he would be leaving the next day, Paul used up his time talking and preaching to the Christians of Troas. In fact, he talked until midnight. At the time, they were meeting in a building, three storeys high. There were many oil lamps burning in these upstairs rooms, to give adequate light to the people meeting there.

Seated in one of the widows, listening to Paul preaching, there was a young man named "Eu-tycus. (pronounced "Eutickus"). Paul talked on, and on, and on. Eutycus was so tired that he fell asleep on the window sill, as the night meeting continued. Eutycus was soon sleeping heavily, when he slipped off the window sill, and fell three storeys to the ground.

Everyone was sure that Eutycus had broken his neck, and that he was dead. Paul went over to the young man, and threw his arms around him. "Do not be afraid" Paul said, "He is alive". Paul then had a meal, and would you believe it, he continued to preach again to the people about the Lord Jesus. He preached all the night through, and left Troas in the morning, when it was daylight. The people took the young man home. He was well, and unhurt by the fall.

Children do not usually like long-winded preachers such as Paul. Children usually like a good story, and no long sermon at the end of it. Maybe, if Paul had children of his own, he might not have talked so long. He must have been very interesting preacher, nevertheless, because the people of Troas loved to hear him speak.

Prayer:

> Lord, our Father in Heaven,
> We thank you for stories about the Apostle Paul.
> Make us faithful hearers of the Word.
> Help us also to be genuine followers of Jesus.
> Forgive us when we fail you.
> Make us all, your faithful servants.   Amen.

Hymn:

I've got peace like a river. (C&P.2. 143), (JP. 120)

Teachers Note: (1) This week we have been thinking about "New Beginnings." At this New Year period, we could all try to make a new start in our Christian life. (2) Paul once hated Christians, afterwards he became a faithful preacher for the Christian Church. (3) Maybe, this Assembly's lesson for young people is, "Do not fall asleep in Church!" There is no need to read a miracle into this story. Maybe the young man fell, just like a cat often falls, loose and relaxed. Reference Acts Chapter 20 verses 7-12. There is something that sounds very human and true about this story.

(a) The Haunted House   *Week 2   Fear*

The children often played together in their avenue. Each house had a garden and a garage. What the children loved about their own avenue, was the fact that no house looked like another one. The houses had all been built at different times, and in different styles of architecture. Most of them had a few trees in the gardens.

However, there was one old house which frightened them. It was a large unpainted house named "The Manor". The people who owned this dark forbidding house had gone to Australia, and they had not returned. So, the Manor house was locked up at all times. The windows were dirty, or broken.

The garden was overgrown with bushes and weeds. During the dark evenings, the children used to run past the old house, because someone said that the house was a "haunted house." At night, the moon shone back as a reflection from some of the windows. The cats crept about in the forsaken garden. The owls used to hoot on top of the roof. Nothing had been painted for many years. The front gates were locked with a rusty old chain. The children all agreed that there must be ghosts inside it. They named it the "Haunted House."

One Spring morning, the children who were on the way to school, saw a large furniture removal van sitting outside the house. Someone had unlocked the rusty chain on the gates. When the children returned from school, the furniture van had gone. Window cleaners were washing the windows. A baby's pram was at the door.

Two sisters, aged 9 and 10 years, named Wendy and Kelly were playing in the garden. A gardener was gathering up weeds, leaves, and broken branches to make a bonfire. The Children realised that a new family had come to live in the so called haunted house.

All that week, and the following week, the painters decorated the rooms, and they even began to paint the window frames and the doors. One day later, the two children, Wendy and Kelly came out to meet the children who were on their way home from school. "Hullo," they shouted, "Would you like to play with us in our garden."

The school children said, "Don't you know, that is a haunted house. We would be too frightened to go inside the gates." Wendy and Kelly laughed. They said, "We may be going to your school next week. Come in and we will let you see our new home." The children trembled with fear, but reluctantly they followed Wendy and Kelly inside.

Every door had been repainted white. Every wall had been decorated with beautiful wall-paper. New carpets were in every room. A baby boy named Bobby was gurgling in his pram in the living room. A friendly fire was burning in the fire-place. There was a rich-looking carpet on the stairs. As Wendy and Kelly showed the six children upstairs, a beautiful young lady, who was the mother of Wendy, Kelly, and Bobby entered the house from the back garden.

She smiled, and said, "Hullo! Children. Have you come to visit us? We are delighted to see you in our new home." She had been baking. She gave the six children, two angel cream cakes each. "We thought that this was a haunted house" the six children said together. Mother pointed to a framed verse hanging on the wall. She said, "You need never be afraid in our home. Just read that verse." The six children read the words.

"Christ is the Head of this house.
The unseen guest at every meal.
The silent listener of every conversation".

Wendy and Kelly, and baby Bobby, sensed that they had gained six good new friends. The six school children never ran past the house in fear again. They somehow felt that there were no such a thing as a haunted house. They believed that if the presence of God filled the house, then that made it a happy home.

Prayer:

Heavenly Father we thank you
for our own homes, and school.
If, we are ever frightened,
teach us that although, we cannot see our Lord,
that he is always near us to keep us safe.
May we have faith in him.   Amen.

Hymn:

Make me a channel of your peace. (C&P.2. 147), (JP. 161)

Teachers' Note: (1) Children are sometimes afraid of darkness. (2) Almost the first lesson in Child Psychology teaches that a baby is born with only two fears. (The fear of a loud noise, and the fear of a sudden fall. All other fears are "learned fears.") (3) There is no such thing as a "haunted house." The presence of God fills everything, and he protects us.

(b) The Imaginative Friend   *Week 2   Fear*

Jennie had been afraid of going to the swimming pool for quite a long time. A year previously, one of the rough boys in the swimming pool had pushed her into the water. Jennie could not swim, so when she fell in, she swallowed water, and suffered an awful fright. The Supervisor at the pool wrote the boy's name and address down in his little black book. He made the boy leave the pool and get dressed. The boy was not allowed to return. Since it happened outside school hours, there was not much more that could be done.

After that, Jennie used to stand beside the pool, when the other children went with their teacher for swimming lessons. The teacher hoped that Jennie would soon recover from her fright. Yet, she always had that fear inside her. She admitted to herself that she hated swimming lessons.

After some weeks had passed, a new girl came from Ireland to live nearby. She was named "Maureen." She had long red hair, dark brown eyes and a big smile. Maureen joined Jennie's class, and the two girls became best friends. Maureen spoke with an Irish accent. She told Jennie about fairies at the bottom of her garden. Maureen told her about seeing the little people, called Leprechauns, (which was an Irish name for elves), who repaired the fairies shoes with tiny little hammers, under the wild flowers in the fields. Her eyes sparkled, as she told Jennie these strange tales. Jennie used to say to Maureen, "My, you have a vivid imagination, Maureen O'Hara, but I love you just the same."

The day the class went to the swimming pool, Jennie said to Maureen, "I am frightened of the water ever since a boy pushed me into the pool," Maureen rolled her eyes around, and she said, "I too am terrified of the water." Jennie said, "Is that not strange, both of us are afraid of the deep water. Let us help each other!"

So Jennie decided to help this strange Irish school friend. She went into the pool at the shallow end, with some of the younger children. They both began to try to swim one breadth of the pool. In the pool, Maureen became a little bit bossy, and encouraged Jennie to try on her back, and after six times moving across, Jennie found that she could float on her own.

Then, Maureen said "Turn over." She held one hand under Jennie's chin, and made Jennie's arms move, and also made her kick with her legs. Jennie was enjoying herself. Soon it was time to go home. She had forgotten about her fear of the water. Next week, the teacher took another twenty of Jennie's class-mates to the pool. Jennie said to Maureen, "Maureen, when are you going to learn to swim. You have been spending most of your time with me?" Maureen said, "As sure as I have seen the little Leprechauns, I am scared of the water!"

Maureen spent the whole lesson teaching Jennie to swim. In a short time, Jennie was swimming breadths of the pool on her own. Later, she could swim lengths. She enjoyed every moment in the water. Maureen just smiled, and said, "Well I can learn next week."

After school was over, one afternoon, Jennie went round to Maureen's house. She went in to meet Maureen's mother, over a cup of tea. As they were all enjoying cake and biscuits, Jennie happened to look up at some certificates in picture frames, which were hanging on the wall. They all were "Special Awards" for Swimming and for Life-saving, presented to Maureen O'Hara in Ireland.

Jenny just looked at Maureen and said, "You could swim all the time, Maureen!" The Irish girl twinkled her brown eyes, and said, "Oh, I forgot to tell you about that. Anyway, a friend in need, is a friend indeed!" Jennie said, "You have such an imagination, Maureen, but I love you. You are still my best friend." Maureen answered, "Jennie, it is just that I love to entertain people."

The problem for the Assembly to solve today is, "Did Maureen tell lies or not?"

Prayer:

> Good Lord, we thank you that our friends
> may help us to lose our inward fears.
> We thank you for the pleasure of learning to swim.
> Help us never to become a bully at school.
> Strengthen all nervous and fearful children.   Amen.

Hymn:

> I've got peace like a river. (C&P.2. 143)

Teachers' Note: (1) Many children carry about little fears inside them. (2) Bullies who cause others' misery, should be reported to a Teacher. (3) A lie-teller is someone who intends to deceive. Was Maureen telling lies, or was she telling stories for fun? (joking or entertainment). Many people who joke, do not smile when they are joking.

(c) I was Afraid

To understand this story, you will need to learn what the word "profit" means. There are two ways, at least, to make money increase. One way is to buy goods at a cheap price, and sell them at a greater price. When Mary buys a pencil from the shop for five pence, and then she sells it to Angela for eight pence. Then Mary has gained three pence more than she had before. (Because eight take-away five leaves three.) That extra three pence is called "profit" or money gained.

There is a second way to gain money. Just lend your money to a bank, and at the end of the year, the bank will pay you "interest." If you lend the bank £10, it may pay you back £12 at the end of the year. So you would have gained £2 more than you had before, because you only began with £10. The extra money is named "interest."

Jesus told a story about interest and profit. A business man was going into a far country for a long time. He called together his servants. To one clever servant, he gave five talents of gold. (A talent was a certain weight of gold or silver). He said to that servant, "Go and do business while I am away. See if you can make a profit for me."

To the second servant, the business man gave two talents of Gold. He said to his second servant, "Go and do business for me, while I am away. Try and make a good profit for me."

To his third servant, he gave one talent of gold. He said to his third servant, "Take this one talent of gold and try to make a profit for me, while I am away."

The business man then went on his journey to the far country. The first servant who had five talents, bought and sold goods, and he made another five talents of profit. Now he had ten talents.

The second servant bought and sold goods, and he made a profit of another two talents. Now he had four talents instead of two.

The third servant took a spade, and he dug a hole in the ground, and he hid his one talent in the ground.

After a long time, the business man returned. He congratulated the first servant, because he had made a profit of five talents. The business man was so pleased, that he promoted the first servant to a higher position. He said, "You have done very well." Come and share the joy of your employer.

He congratulated the second servant, because he had made a profit of two talents. "Well done" he said. "You have been faithful over less important matters. I will promote you to a higher position in my employment. Enter into the joy of your employer.

Then the third servant which had buried his talent of gold in the ground, came to the business man and said, "I knew that you were a hard man, reaping where you have not sown. I was afraid. Therefore I buried your talent in the ground. Here it is back again." The business man replied to his servant. "You are a lazy man. If you knew that I expected profit from my talent of gold, why did you not lend it to the bank or to the money changers. They would have paid you interest at the end of each year.

The business man took the talent from the third servant and he gave it to the first servant, who had already made a profit of five talents for his employer. Then the Business man said, a very strange but true statement. "To the person who has will be given more, and he will have an abundance. Whoever has nothing, even what he has shall be taken away from him." The business man dismissed his third servant from his employment.

The third servant had been afraid to use his talent, so he hid it, and he gained nothing. Today, we use the word "talent" to mean our own personal gifts and skills given to us by God. If we are good at sport, or art, or arithmetic, or English, then we must develop that talent, or it will fade away. We will be left without any skills, if we do not practise them. That is how we gain profit from school work. That is how we gain in life. Everyone is good at something. Do not allow fear to hold you back from trying to do better.

Prayer:
> Lord teach us to use all our talents,
> and so may we increase our skills.
> Help us to spend our time in the most useful way
> for the enjoyment of God's wonderful world,
> for the service of others,
> and for learning about life.
> Through Jesus Christ our Lord.   Amen.

Hymn:
> Come and praise the Lord our King. (JP. 34)

Teachers' note: (1) Personal talents are a gift from God. (2) Personal talents may be developed. (3) Children sometimes have little fears about developing skills.

(a) Mother Teresa

One of God's good people in our lifetime, was Agnes Gonxha Bojaxhiu. She was born in Yugoslavia, in the year 1910. She is much better known to us as Mother Teresa. Agnes was a Roman Catholic. From the age of about twelve years, Agnes felt called to spend her life in the service of God.

Agnes went to Ireland to become a Loreta Nun in Dublin, when she was about 17. When her early training was finished, she was sent to India, as a Novice. (Someone whose was still in training to be a Nun.) When she finished her training, and took her final vows, she took the name of Teresa, because St. Teresa was her favourite Saint.

Teresa became a geography teacher in a school in Calcutta. She taught the children of rich families, and she did it very well indeed. The Catholic school was very near the poorest part of the city. A famine had struck their country villages, and the poor native families had to get food somehow. They had been forced by their poverty and starvation, to come into the great city of Calcutta. These poor people became beggars, They were starving for food and they needed clothing. Their homes were made up of huts and cardboard boxes.

Teresa felt the call of God to work with the poorest people. However, she had to wait for two years, before she was released by the Church for this kind of social work. She, first of all, had to become trained as a nurse. Then, Teresa returned back to Calcutta. She began to treat the poor sick people in a small room. She also taught the street beggar children to read and to write. She taught them to wash themselves every day. She knew that health and good hygiene go together. (Cleanliness comes next to Godliness).

When other Nuns came to assist her in her work, Teresa called them "Sisters." The Calcutta Council Authorities gave her a larger room beside a Hindu Temple. She named the place for the sick people of the streets, the "Place of the Pure in Heart."

Teresa was allowed to organise a new Order, called "The Missionaries of Charity." Church people from all over the world sent gifts of money for her work. Teresa built "Homes for the Dying", and "Homes for Children". It was in 1979 that Teresa was awarded the "Nobel Peace Prize" for her useful work for the poor people of India.

Mother Teresa did not ever press anyone to become a Christian. Of course, the Sisters conducted Church Services every day, and anyone was free to attend, and to learn about Christianity. Instead, Sister Teresa nursed the sick people of any religion. Many of those people who were dying, were cared for in her hospital homes, because Sister Teresa realised, that such a home might have been the only place they had ever been, where anyone had ever loved them.

Mother Teresa and her fellow Sisters knew that the poor people of India were not themselves to blame for their poverty and sickness. They could not help being born at such a time, nor in such a place. She loved the poor people with all her heart. She knew that she too would grow old, and therefore, she prayed that many more of India's young people would become Nurses and Doctors. In that way they could help the poor back to better health.

Mother Teresa, indeed, grew older, and died at the age of 87 years, on the 5th September 1997. The Indian Nation gave her the honour of a State Funeral, because everyone loved her for the good work she had been doing.

Prayer:

> Lord of all the world, and Father of all people,
> We thank you for the missionary Nurse,
> whom we know as Mother Teresa.
> We pray for all poor people,
> and for the children of the world.
> Bless them all, teach them to read and to write.
> May they hear of Jesus, who also loved the poor.   Amen.

Hymn:

> Lead me from death to life. (C&P.2. 140),
> or Bind us together Lord. (JP. 17)

Teachers' Note: (1) Mother Teresa was once a little girl. She must have been a very devout Christian. (2) Mother Teresa first of all, was thoroughly trained to help sick and poor people. Training is important. (3) Mother Teresa, was only one of many people who have spent their lives in the service of the sick and the poor of India.

(b) The Bagpipes   *Week 3   More Social Needs*

Have you ever seen the Scottish pipe band marching down the street, with their kilts swinging, and their bagpipes playing, and their drums rolling? It is a very inspiring sight to watch. Every Scottish Clan has it own tartan plaid. The plaid is a specially woven cloth. Scots people are very proud of their Clan tartan. The proper tartan to wear depends on your name, and the Clan or Sept (family) to which your forefathers belonged.

There is the Royal Stewart tartan, which is red, and the McLeod tartan which is mostly yellow. The Campbells, the McDonalds, the Frazers, the McGreggors, the McKenzies, all possess their own beloved tartan plaids. Originally, the tartan plaid was very like a big blanket that a Scotsman threw around himself, to keep him warm, when he had to lie overnight on the heather.

Most Scots-people love the sound of the, "Pibroch," which is known better to English people as the "bagpipes". Many songs and even hymns can be played on the bag-pipes. Boys and girls who watch television, will remember hearing the hymn, "Amazing Grace" being played on the bagpipes. Another one of the well known older bagpipe tunes is called "The Campbells are coming". It used to be played by the pipers of the British army as a marching tune.

In the year 1857 there was a war in India, known as "The Indian Mutiny." The mutiny against the British began, because the sepoys (Indian soldiers) were ordered to use cow and pig fat to grease their rifles. To the Hindus, a cow is a sacred animal, and so the Hindu soldiers felt that this went against their religious beliefs. The Muslim religion does not use pork (pig meat). So the Sepoys rebelled around the city of Lucknow. They killed many of the British people who lived in that area. Even women and children, who were the families of the soldiers, were killed in the war.

The British people who remained, barricaded themselves inside the walls of Lucknow. They were utterly cut off from the rest of the world. They prayed for help. Many had been wounded. Everyone was starving with hunger. The sick, and dying lay on the stone floors behind the walls.

The Indian troops were outside the walls, fighting under the leadership of Nana Sahib the Indian General. The only thing that kept the soldiers, and two hundred British women and children safe, was that the gates of the city had been locked and barred. Eventually, the message of the desperate plight of the people in Lucknow reached the ears of the British Commander in another city. In order to rescue the besieged people, the British troops under the command of Sir Colin Campbell, made a fast march across the Indian countryside, to try and reach Lucknow in time.

Inside the city, the wounded, the sick, and the dying lay behind the walls. One Scots lady who had been lying for weeks on the floor with the others, suddenly sat up. She shouted out to the other British people around, in her Scottish dialect, "Dinnae you hear the pipes of Havland sounding?" The people became very quiet. They listened. Sure enough, somewhere far away, they heard the sound of the bagpipes, and the drums were rolling. The British troops were coming at a quick march to rescue them.

As the troops drew nearer, they came in hundreds, marching ranks of three abreast, with the pipers and drummers at the front. The British people who had been besieged, swung open the great city gates, and the pipers and soldiers marched through them. The pipers had been playing a well known Scottish tune, "The Campbells are Coming." The rescue was complete. The British troops took the women and children away to a safer place. The rescued people never forgot the tune, "The Campbells are coming."

Can you suggest what were some of the social needs of the people in this particular situation. The British people known as civilians, (or people of the city),who were barricaded behind the walls, longed for peace. Many of the women and children were afraid for their lives. They had lost all hope. It was the sound of the bagpipes in the distance that brought them the hope of being rescued. Can you think of any other social needs that the native people of India might have had, at this time? (Peace, food, water, friendship, houses, employment etc.)

Music can do many good things for us. Music has a social function. Music can make us relax. Music may make us happy. Music can help us to worship God. Music can entertain us, and help us to express feelings that lie deep in our hearts. Music has a great power to make a number of separate human beings into a united company. (A choir or a Pop Group). Just think how the Salvation Army used music to spread their message of hope to the poorest people of what was once known as "Darkest England." What would a school be like without a piano?

Prayer:

Lord of all peace, we pray that wars may cease.
Bless people all over the world.
We especially pray for poor people,
and children of the third world.
Grant to them food, help and healing.
May Doctors and Nurses be trained,
for their peaceful work.   Amen.

Hymn:

Praise the Lord in the rhythm of your music, (C&P.1. 33),
or, Praise him on the trumpet, (JP. 200)

Teachers' Note: Care will need to be given to keep this Assembly simple enough for the pupils age range. Warfare brings social needs for people on both sides of a conflict. This includes the native population in the story. (1) Let us pray for peace in the world. (2) The women and children of Lucknow had hope, when they heard the music of the bagpipes. It reminded them that they were safe. Can you think of any other music that has brought peace of mind to people. (Salvation Army Band) Church organs, School piano). (3) India had now become a great industrial nation in her own right. Today she rules her own people, and is tackling many of her own social needs.

(c) The Great Catch of Fish

St. Luke tells the story about the occasion when Jesus was preaching to the people beside the lake. There were two boats nearby, and the fishermen were washing their nets. Jesus went into one of the boats, and he sat down in the boat, and taught the people who were standing on the shore.

Then Jesus said to Simon Peter, "Put out into the deeper water, and let down your nets for a catch." Simon Peter replied, "Master, we have worked hard all night, and we have not caught anything. But if you say so, I will let down the nets."

They sailed out into the lake and let down their nets. When they did so, their nets became filled with fish. There were so many fish, that their nets began to break. They called their companions in the other fishing boat, to help them. They soon filled both boats with fish.

When Simon Peter saw the great catch of fish, he fell down on his knees before Jesus, and said, "Go away from me, Lord, because I am a sinful man." Peter had never caught so many fish before. James and John, who were Peter's partners, were watching everything that was happening. Jesus said to them, "Do not be afraid, from now onward you will become fishers of men." (people).

The Church is like a net gathering people together. Jesus said these words to them, because he knew that they were going to become his disciples. Christian disciples are like fishermen.

Although they had been seamen all their lives, Peter, James and John pulled their boats up on the shore. They left them behind. They became followers of Jesus.

Was this a miracle? How do you think that Jesus knew where the shoal of fishes were? Maybe, he was watching the seagulls circling around the movement of the fish out in the lake, just as any good fisherman might do. Maybe, that is why Jesus stopped teaching the people at that time. There is a time to teach, and a time to catch fish. St. Luke was a doctor, and it was he who wrote about this happening.

The sign of the fish in the days of the early church, was a secret sign that the person using the sign was a Christian. When the Christian slaves used to meet in Rome, they were persecuted. They held their meetings in the "catacombs", which were the underground grave tunnels below the city. If you ever visit Rome, be sure to look out for the sign of the fish, drawn on the walls of the catacombs.

Prayer:

> Lord of heaven and earth,
> we thank you for the Lord Jesus,
> and for his teaching about God's love.

We pray for the church world-wide.
Bless Christians everywhere, especially children.
We pray for Christian schools and their Staffs.   Amen.

Hymn:

Waves are beating on the shore. (C&P.2. 84)

Teachers' Note: (1) Jesus was a dark skinned man, similar to an Arab from the near Eastern countries. He probably would have had brown eyes and black hair. (2) Jesus loved to help everyone. This is why he taught and healed the people. His main message was about God's love for people. (3) Strangely, Jesus never chose shepherds to be his disciples. Instead, he chose fishermen. Maybe that was because they were used to working together. Christians should work together, because they serve the one Lord Jesus.

(a) A Fishy Story

Week 4   On Trust

Daniel's Granny was going away on Holiday. She invited Daniel round to her house, and asked him, whether he would be willing to feed her goldfish, while she was away. She gave Daniel the key of the house, and explained that she would only be on holiday for about ten days. Granny explained, that all Daniel had to do was to open the back door, with her key. He was to feed the goldfish with a few pinches of fish food from a round tin, morning and evening. Daniel agreed to faithfully feed the fish, if she would bring him back a surprise present, when she came home. Granny agreed to the deal.

Off Granny went next day, and that evening, Daniel opened her back door with his key, and fed the fish with the fish-food, from the tin. The fish food seemed to be made up of dried dead flies or moths. Next morning Daniel went to school, but he forgot to feed the goldfish, which was swimming about in the glass tank on Granny's oak side-board. Worse still, he forgot that evening as well. Indeed, Daniel completely forgot the poor little fish for about nine days.

One morning in the school Assembly, the Teacher was reading from St. John chapter 21, about Jesus talking to Peter. Jesus said, "Peter, feed my sheep: feed my lambs: and again, feed my sheep." Teacher asked the children, "Why do you think that Jesus repeated these words three time to Peter?" One bright girl, Diane, raised her hand, and said, "Because Peter denied his Lord, three times, Miss." "That is a very good answer," replied the Teacher. Another boy, named Bernard, gave another answer. Bernard said, "Because people forget things so easily, Miss. Three times gives us no excuse, Miss!"

At that moment, Daniel stopped day-dreaming. He heard the teacher read aloud, once more, "Feed my sheep. Feed my Lambs. Feed my sheep."

"Crikey," he said to himself, Granny said it three times too, "Feed my fish!" I must have forgotten all about that goldfish!" Daniel's heart was beating very quickly.

After school, Daniel ran home, collected the key, and then he ran to his Granny's back door. He opened the door, and he looked into the kitchen at the fish tank. There was the poor starved fish floating with its tail up, and its head down. The disaster had happened. The fish was dead! What could Daniel do now? He scratched his head, and thought, and thought, and thought!

Then Daniel had a brainwave. He remembered that the travelling fun-fair was visiting the town, and that it was in the local park for a few days. He knew that often the fairground people gave prizes of goldfish in a clear plastic bag filled with water.

Daniel spent nearly two pounds throwing rings, that did not seem to stay on the hooks on the stall. The stall-minder watched Daniel quietly crying to himself, and he felt sorry for Daniel. "Here Son," he said, "Here is a goldfish for trying so hard to get the rings on the hooks." Daniel could hardly believe his ears. Daniel thanked the stall-minder with all his heart. He ran all the way back to Granny's house. He carefully emptied the new goldfish into Granny's fish tank. "Granny would never know what had happened," he thought. All was well!

Granny arrived back next day. She said, "I couldn't get a present that you would really like at the sea-side, so I will just take you down town today, and I will buy you a mountain bike as your surprise present. Daniel felt awful. The last person he ever wanted to deceive, was his kind Granny. They went down the road in the bus, and Granny bought the mountain bike for him. It was a beautiful bike, red and gold in colour, and covered in packing paper. They walked back, and Daniel pushed the bike.

Daniel felt awful inside. At last he told Granny everything that had happened. How he had forgotten to feed the goldfish, and had found another one at the fun fair. Granny did not seem surprised. She just said, "Daniel, I am proud of you. You have told the truth. Any boy who tells the truth deserves a mountain bike."

She said "You see, Daniel, I knew all the time that this fish, was not Goldie, my fish. You see, I have had him for seven years. I taught him to come to the left-hand side of the fish tank, when I tapped the glass. He came if he was hungry. This new fish is just getting to know me. He is just learning." Daniel and his Granny hugged each other. They never forgot Jesus' words to Peter, "Feed my sheep. Feed my Lambs. Feed my sheep." Granny said, "If Jesus forgave Peter three times, why should I not forgive you. I would trust you anywhere." Granny was always a good sport!

Prayer:

> Loving Heavenly Father, we may fail you,
> by our thoughtless way of life.
> Forgive us, as Jesus forgave St. Peter.
> Teach us the responsibility of being trusted.
> We pray for people who fail in life.
> We pray for drop outs, and people in prison.   Amen.

Hymn:

> He gave me eyes so I could see. (C&P.1. 18), (JP. 74)

Teachers' Note: (1) St. Peter denied that he ever knew Jesus, three times. He told three whopping lies! (2) Jesus freely forgave Peter, and he never held a grudge against him. (3) Daniel felt that to tell a lie to his Granny, was to tell a lie to someone who loved him with all her heart. He just could not do it. God loves us all!

(b) Polycarp

Week 4   On Trust

In the early days of the Roman Empire, many of the Christians were slaves. The Roman Emperor, was known as "Caesar" which means "The Leader". The early Caesars were pagans. They did not believe in Christ. In order to keep people of the Roman Empire together under Caesar's power, he instituted a religion in which people had to worship the Emperor, and say, "Caesar is Lord" in public.

The Christians believed that Jesus was Lord, and that he must have the highest honour, even more than the Emperor. So they refused to say "Caesar is Lord." Often, the Christians were slaves. To avoid capture, they used to meet in underground caverns, known as the "catacombs" where the Romans buried their dead. They held their Christian services in secret.

One of the Caesars was named Nero. Historians think that he was either very bad or very mad. Some people set Rome on fire one night, and the city was nearly burned down, because many of the buildings were made of wood. Nero blamed the Christians for causing the fire. He decided to wipe the Christians out. He made his soldiers kill as many Christians as they could find. To find out whether a person was a Christian, that person was asked to offer a gift to the Emperor and to say, "Caesar is Lord." Christians always refused to use these words about an earthly King. (Even though they respected the State and Law and order).

Christian history records the story of the famous martyr, the Bishop of Smyrna whose name was "Polycarp". He was an old man, who could still remember

St. John the Apostle, being alive. Polycarp died about the year A.D. 155. He must have been born in the first century.

When the authorities asked him to offer a gift to the Emperor, and to say, "Caesar is Lord," he refused. His reply to the persecutors is a very famous one. He said,

"Eighty and six years have I served him, (Jesus).
and he has done me no wrong.
How then can I blaspheme my King and Saviour?

("Blaspheme" means to speak against someone.)

The soldiers arrested Bishop Polycarp, the aged Christian preacher, and tied him to a stake, which had been hammered into the ground. They placed dried bushes and pieces of wood around him, as high his shoulders. Then they set the wood alight, and so they wickedly burned Polycarp to death. Polycarp became a Christian martyr (witness). Polycarp loved Jesus so much, that he could not deny his true Lord, even though it cost him his life. How easy it is today to be a Christian!

Prayer:

Heavenly Father we give you thanks
for the faith and bravery of Polycarp.
We give you thanks for the long line
of people down through history,
who died for their faith.
Give us, O Lord, the courage
to confess our faith in Jesus.   Amen.

Hymn. He's got the whole world in his hands. (C&P.1. 19), (JP. 78)

Teachers Note: (1) In the early days of the Christian Church, people had to be willing to die for their faith in Jesus. (2) Polycarp was an aged man of eighty-six. (3) Polycarp is an example of true faith to us all. We are all called to be martyrs in the original meaning of the word, which is to be a "witness" for our faith.

(c) Jesus in the Synagogue

Week 4   On Trust

The Temple in Jerusalem was the large central place of worship for Jews during the time when Jesus was alive. However, many villages in Judea also had a Synagogue building, which was a place for meeting and worship, for Jewish people. The word, "Synagogue" really means an "assembly".

One day Jesus went to the village of Nazareth, the village where he had been brought up, as a boy. It was his usual custom on the Sabbath day to attend the village synagogue. It was customary also, that someone read the Holy Scriptures. Jesus stood up to read, (note that in those days, not everyone could read). The Minister gave to him the scroll of Isaiah the prophet. Jesus turned to the place, which we now know as Chapter 61, verse 1. He read the words,

"The Spirit of the Lord is on me,
because he has anointed me
to preach good tidings to the poor.
He has sent me to proclaim freedom
for prisoners,
and recovery of sight for the blind,
to release the oppressed;
to proclaim the year of the Lord's favour."

Then, he rolled up the scroll of Isaiah the prophet, and gave it back to the minister, and he sat down. Jesus said, "Today, this Scripture is fulfiled in your ears." The people who were listening were amazed and pleased by his gracious words. They said to each other, "Is this not Joseph's son?" They could not understand, how someone, who had been a local village boy, could speak with such kind and gracious knowledge. Jesus gave them a good answer, when he replied that, "No prophet is accepted as a prophet in his home town!" Sometimes we do not see what is before our own eyes.

Luke was a writer and a Doctor. He tells us about another occasion, when Jesus was in the Synagogue. There was a man there whose mind was disturbed (also described in those days, as being filled with evil powers). The man kept on shouting out in the Synagogue, "What do you want with us, Jesus of Nazareth? Have you come to destroy us? I know who you are, the holy man of God."

Jesus spoke to the man, very firmly, "Keep quiet! Evil spirit, come out of him!" Suddenly, the man was thrown to the floor, as if by a strong force. Then, he became still. He had been instantly healed by Jesus. The noisy man became quite normal. The congregation were amazed at this healing, and asked among themselves, "What kind of teaching is this? This man, Jesus, has the power to give orders to evil spirits, and they come out!" The news of the power of Jesus to heal, spread about everywhere.

Clearly, even though the man who had been healed, had been described previously as having been possessed by an evil spirit, he had been suffering from some form of mental illness. The important fact is that Jesus brought the poor man relief and healing.

Now for another story. Dr. Magill always went to church on a Sunday morning, if he was free to do so. He liked to sit with his wife. Usually, he had so many calls out to sick people, that he loved to have a quiet hour in the Church, taking part in the Service. Mrs. Poplar was one of the church members, who was always talking in church, when she should have been quiet. She was always gossiping about somebody.

The previous Saturday night, she had eaten fish and chips. She felt ill after she went to bed, so she drank a bottle of lemonade. On Sunday morning she went off to church, and as soon as she got into the church, turning backwards in her pew, she began to tell Mrs. Parker, in the pew behind, about the pains in her stomach. People sitting in the other pews could hear Mrs. Poplar gossipping as usual. During the second hymn, when people were singing together in worship, Mrs. Poplar felt more pains in her tummy, and then she fainted and collapsed on the floor.

Everyone looked at Dr. Magill. The good Doctor slipped out of his own seat, and went to help Mrs. Poplar. The people continued singing. Dr. Magill took a little bottle of liquid from his pocket, and held it to Mrs. Poplar's nose. Suddenly, Mrs. Poplar opened her eyes. "Oh, I am embarrassed," she said. "Everyone is looking at me". Dr. Magill, told her to take another sniff of the little bottle of liquid. She did so, and then she made such a loud sneeze, that everyone looked around at her.

Dr. Magill did not tell her off. Mrs. Parker whispered to the Doctor that Mrs. Poplar had been eating fish and chips, and drinking lemonade, the night before. He was smiling, and always very understanding. He whispered, "Now, Mrs. Poplar, no more eating fish and chips at night, and no more drinking lemonade in the middle of the night in bed." Mrs. Poplar wondered how the Doctor knew about what had made her ill. Dr. Magill never enlightened her. The important thing was that noisy Mrs. Poplar was better again. Can you see any likeness between what happened in the Synagogue, and what happened in the church that day?

Prayer:

> Father of all people, everywhere,
> we thank you for the wisdom of Jesus.
> We thank you for his power and authority over evil.
> Grant to us all the grace
> to resist the temptation to speak wrongly.
> We pray for anyone who has a mental illness.
> Bless all Doctors and Nurses.   Amen.

Hymn:

> Fill thou my life, O Lord my God. (C&P.1. 41)

Teachers' Note: (1) Attending the synagogue, assembly, or church is a good habit. It teaches us our faith, religion, and what is known as "culture". (eg. Scripture, good music, and self-discipline). (2) The church is for everyone, even those who regard themselves as "sinners," or even those who may feel unwanted.

(3) Mrs. Poplar, was noisy, like the man in the synagogue. She could not heal herself, just like the man in the synagogue. The Doctor was like Jesus, he made Mrs. Poplar well again.

(a) Robin Redbreast

Legends are stories told by people long ago. These stories are passed down from father to son, and from mother to daughter. Here is a Red Indian legend about how the Robin red-breast came to America. You will find that the poet Whittier wrote about the legend in one of his poems.

Once upon a time, there was a famous Red Indian chief. He had a young son, who had become a "teen-ager". Every Indian boy longs to become a fully recognised "brave" in the Indian tribe. This means that he is recognised as a man, and is no longer considered to be a boy. The great Chief wanted his son to become a famous brave, able to fight, and to hunt wild animals without fear.

Each boy had to go through a test, before he could change from being a "Tenderfoot" to a warrior. The test meant that the boy was left alone in an Indian hut in the dark forest, for seven days. The chief's young son, was not interested in killing people in battle. He did not want to become a warrior. He loved the countryside. He loved the birds in the sky, and the fish in the sea. He loved the wild flowers.

Yet, like the other boys, when he became of age, he was not afraid to go through the Test. He lived alone in the hut for seven days, proving that he was brave in himself. On the seventh day, the great Chief, made a hot meal, with venison he had taken from the deer, which he had hunted and killed. He brought it to his young son in the hut in the dark forest.

However, when the Chief looked into the hut, he found the boy lying dead. He had quietly died in his sleep, during the dark hours of the seventh night. Later, they dug his grave, and laid the young Indian boy in the ground. They put his bow and arrows beside him. They also placed his pipe, and Indian knife, and his wampum braid, which he had worn around his hair, in the grave beside him, and covered his body with earth.

As they buried the young Indian boy, suddenly, a strange little bird appeared, and roosted on the roof of the hut. The bird had brown feathers on its back, and more bright red feathers on its chest. It was the Robin Red-breast, (which was larger than the British Robin).

Strangely, the bird spoke to the Indian Chief, and to the other Red Indians. Strangely too, it spoke with a human voice, just this once. The Robin said, "I a bird, am still your Son. I am happier now, than if I was a hunter, or a brave, or a warrior. Each day, I shall welcome the morning sun at the door of your wigwams. Each day I will sing in the corn field, and in the wheat field. I shall sing about the coming Spring. Even in the snow, every child shall know my voice. I will sing of lovely things; about kindness and beauty."

The Robin spoke on, "Whenever you hear a Robin red-breast singing, you will always remember, that gentleness is better than fighting wars. The Indian who praises, is happier than the Indian who hates. The person who sings is happier than the warrior who kills." The Robin Red breast was never known to speak in a human voice again. He flew away, and may be found, darting here and there in any American bush.

Each time an Indian sees a Robin Redbreast, he is reminded that some boys have a gentle side to their character. There are boys who love beautiful things, such as the blue-bell, or the primrose. They love to watch the eagle high in the sky. They love to think about salmon-fish swimming across the world's oceans, just to later swim back to their home river upstream Many healthy normal boys love music, painting, and books and poetry. Most of all, they love the little bird we call "the Robin Redbreast."

Prayer:

> Heavenly Father, we thank you
> for the legend of the Robin Redbreast.
> help us to respect each other,
> for what we are in ourselves.
> Teach us the value of music, poetry, and of hymns.
> Help us to learn the meaning of culture, and religion.
> For Robin redbreasts, we give you our praise.   Amen.

Hymn:

Morning has broken. (C&P.1. 1) (JP. 166)

Teachers' Note: (1) A legend is a story with a meaning in it. We never ask "Is a legend true? "We always ask, "What truth does the Legend teach?" (2) We are all made differently. Some children hate sport, others love it. Some children love music, and singing, others are not interested. Some are aggressive, and could easily become bullies. Some children like to help other children, and easily make good friends. (3) We do not all grow up to be what our parents might want us to be. Yet we could give them a good surprise!

(b) The Leprechaun

In the many farm houses and whitewashed cottages in Ireland, they burn large peat fires in their hearths. In the days before television was invented, the Irish family, and any visitors who happened to be there, used to sit around the blazing fire, in the dark evening hours of Winter. They burned an oil lamp on the table, because they did not have electricity. They often told stories about fairies, and the "little people" whom they called "Leprechauns".

Now we must learn the difference between a story out of the Bible, and a story which is a Legend. Irish people believe the Bible stories, but they love to tell the old Legends, handed down, from family to family, for more than a thousand years. These old Legends have a truth embedded in them, somewhere in the story.

Here is the story of a clever little Leprechaun. Now, Leprechauns were supposed to be tiny little people, who spent their days, as little shoe-makers (cobblers). The Leprechaun makes his little shoes, and he or she is said to sing happily from morning until night. The Irish say that if you ever come across a little fellow tapping away with his tiny hammer, making a pair of little fairy shoes in some lonely field or mountainside, you must never take your eyes of him, even for a fraction of a moment, else he will be gone.

Patrick went out one Winter's night, and to his great delight, he spied a Leprechaun. The tiny little man wore a scarlet cap, and a coat of green. He hammered, and sang with with his tiny voice, and a cruiskeen (a wine jar) lay by his side. Patrick laughed to himself, because he had seen a Leprechaun at last. But the fairy was laughing too!

With an eager grasp, Patrick caught the elf in his hand, and he said to him, "Give me your fairy purse," (which was said to be full of gold). The little Leprechaun replied, "I've given my purse away to the lady by your side". Patrick took his eyes off the little man, to look for the lady by his side, and as he looked away, in a moment, the elf was gone! Patrick realised that he had been tricked. He had taken his eyes off the Leprechaun. He had lost the fairy gold. Patrick told his friends later, then he laughed to think of the fool he had been. Not far away, underneath the Dandelions in the hayfield, the fairy was laughing too !"

Parents tell their children this story, to warn them, never to take their eyes off their good aims and ideals. Like the archer, with his bow and arrow, we must not take our eyes of the target. Jesus once said, "Happy are the pure in heart, for they shall see God."

Prayer:

> Father, help us to find the good meaning
> from the stories of our imagination.
> Teach us from the parables of Jesus.

Teach us to keep our eyes fixed on Jesus,
as our supreme example.
May we realise that others are always watching us.   Amen.

Hymn:

He who would valiant be. (C&P.1. 44), (JP. 80)

Teachers' Note: (1) There are really no such little people as Leprechauns, or fairies. Patrick lost the little fairy man, because he did not pay enough attention. School is a place where we must give attention to learning. (2) We may find lessons about life from old Legends. Did you notice the good figure and the bad figure in the last Pantomime you have seen? (3) How many words can you find that mean "To See". (Watch, stare, look, gaze, observe, peer, view, study, perceive, understand, dream, imagine ... and there are many more!)

(c) The Bramble King   *Week 5   Legends*

Here is a Legend from the Book of Judges, (which is the seventh book of the Bible). This story imagines that the trees had a language, and that they held conversations with each other. One day the trees decided to choose a king over them. They said to the Olive-tree, "Will you be our king?" The Olive-tree, replied, "Why should I give up my oil which is useful to everyone, to rule over the trees?" So, he did not become king.

The trees asked the Fig-tree to be their king. The Fig-tree replied, "Why should I give up my fruit, which others say is so good and nourishing, to rule over the trees." So he did not become king.

Then, the trees asked the Vine-tree (grows grapes) to become king of the trees. The Vine-tree answered, "Why should I give up my grapes and wine, which makes everyone happy, to become king of the trees." The Vine tree did not become king.

Next, the trees asked the Bramble-bush (Blackberry bush) to become their king. The Bramble-bush answered, "If you really want me to be your king, then come and put your trust under my shade. If you will not do that, then fire will come out of the Bramble-bush and destroy you." That day, the Bramble became king of the trees.

What does this Legend mean? First, it carries a meaning about people. Many expert, educated, and good people are already serving others in the Community, so that they have not the time to give, or to accept responsibility, for keeping law and order. The trees were all too busy to accept responsibility. This is neither good nor bad. It is just how things are in life.

Secondly, the Bramble-bush was the lowest and most common of all the trees. He said that he was willing to become king of the trees, if the other trees would give him their loyalty and trust. If not, fire would come out of the Bramble bush, and as in a forest fire, all the other trees would be destroyed. Leadership demands loyalty from others. Fire only begins when trees and bushes become tinder dry. Accidental forest fires begin low on the ground. The Bramble being the lowest of the trees would be in a good position to warn the other trees, but he insisted in loyalty from the other trees. (Just like the Captain of a football Team, or a hockey team).

The other trees chose the lowliest and most common tree of all to be their king. Brambles grow wild anywhere, and they only produce Blackberries. The meaning of this is that even the most ordinary boy or girl, if they are prepared and willing, may reach the highest place of responsibility in this life. Jesus used to say that the first shall be last, and the last shall be first. The Bible also says that "A little child shall lead them." Strong character helps people to rely upon us as individuals who make good Leaders.

Prayer:

> Teach us good Lord, the meaning
> of the Bramble Legend.
> Show us that many of us are needed
> to serve the community. .
> Help us to acquire those good qualities,
> that in time, we also may be willing to be leaders.
> Bless those weaker people,
> who may always lean on others.   Amen.

Hymn:

> My faith it is an oaken staff. (C&P.1. 46), (JP. 168)

Teachers' Note: (1) Many people are busy, helpfully serving the community. (2) Ordinary people may be called upon to lead others. (3) If someone is willing to be our leader, and to accept responsibilities for us, then, the least we can offer them is our support and loyalty. *Reference Judges Chapter 9, verses 8-15.*

(a) The Igloo

Week 6   Danger

Many years ago, Kimo was an Eskimo. He lived in snowy Alaska, in the Arctic circle, where the sea freezes over, for long periods of the Winter. Kimo was just ten years of age. He lived with his Mum and Dad, and his young sister, in an ice house, called an 'igloo'. The igloo was the shape of a ball cut in two, and turned upside down. His Dad had made the igloo, cutting out blocks of frozen snow, and building the large snow bricks together.

As well as being the shape of a ball, cut in half, and turned up-side down, the igloo also had only one door, just low enough for Kimo and family to crawl into, walking on their knees. There was also a long tunnel, also made of snow, just the height of the door, but much smaller than the height of the igloo.

Kimo asked his Dad, why they lived in such a strange shaped house. "Dad said, "Kimo, there are no trees where we live, here among the snowy plains and hills. So we use snow for bricks, because it is free, and it lies all around us. We make our house the shape of a half up-turned ball, because the blizzards are so strong here, that they would blow an ordinary house down. The worst storms, blow round the ice walls, and pass by. The snow becomes ice very quickly. So our house is very strong. It is also quite warm inside, and we leave a small hole in the roof, to allow the smoke from our fire, and the oil lamp fumes to get away."

The inside of the igloo was quite snug. There were animal skins on the floor, and the roof was high enough, for anyone to stand upright. It was just like living in a circular room. Inside, there were oil lamps, and a stove for cooking. They had no television, but they had several radios, and a radio telephone.

"Kimo watched his Dad building the long snow tunnel up to the door. "Dad, why do you build the tunnel so low, that we have to crawl inside.? Dad told Kimo that the entrance was built that long low shape, to keep out the big polar bears, which roamed the icelands. "They are too big to get inside the tunnel. If you ever see a polar bear, run for the tunnel, if you do not have your rifle with you." If a polar bear put his nose inside too far, then our husky dogs would see him off, in such a small space."

Kimo was learning fast, how to survive in the icelands. One day, Kimo was fishing with his rod and line, after making a hole in the ice. It was so easy pulling out the big fishes, from the sea below the ice that he forgot to keep a watch behind him. Suddenly, a great white bear appeared He was a very hungry bear, and was out hunting for his dinner. Kimbo tried to remember, what his Dad had taught him. "Do not panic. Use your head! Only use your rifle to kill the bear, if you are in mortal danger. Get the dogs between you and the polar bear. Get back inside the igloo, if you can."

Kimo remembered it again, "Do not panic. Use your head." Kimo looked at his fishes lying on the snow. He took three of them, and threw them at the bear, while he picked up his rifle, and ran for the safety of the igloo. The bear immediately smelt the fish, lying before him, and he turned aside to eat them. This allowed Kimo time to escape. He scuffled on his knees into the igloo tunnel. Just as he was rushing inside, he noticed his Dad, with his gun at the ready, watching the bear. He smiled at Kimo. "Let the bear go, there is no need to kill him," Dad said.

"He will go away, after he has eaten the fish. The husky dogs were barking loudly. Dad fired a shot into the air with his rifle, and the big white bear moved off, and he never came back again. Kimo had learnt another lesson in the snow. When things go wrong, "Keep calm.""

What would you have done, if you were in similar circumstances? Remembering that the bear was quite a distance away. Would you have shot the bear? Would you have stood still with fright? Would you have started crying? Would you have turned your back on the Bear and run away. Would you have copied Kimo, and thrown the fishes, to distract the bear's attention.

The good thing about this story is that whatever Kimo had done, he was always quite safe, because Kimo's father, was watching everything, ready to protect his son from danger. Dad, being an Eskimo, knew that even Polar Bears had cubs to protect, and they too had needed food in Winter, just like the Eskimos. Kimo said his prayers that evening, and slept safely in the igloo that night. He cuddled up beside his two great husky dogs, Rover and Ranger. He knew that was safe!

Prayer:

> Lord of all creation,
> we pray for people overseas.
> We pray for children of other lands.
> Guard them from danger,
> and heal them when they are sick.
> We pray for every member of our own school.
> Help us all to remember,
> what we have been taught.   Amen.

Hymn:

Peace perfect peace. (C&P.1. 53)

Teachers' Note: (1) Every family needs a good home. We must not take our homes for granted. Let us be thankful. (2) Every family may meet sudden danger. No one is to panic, but rather to keep brave in heart. (3) A family should always help each other! Always!

(b) Look before you Leap

Week 6   Danger

The Gas pumping station was quite near the school. It was surrounded by steel railings, with sharp points at the top. The sign read, "Dangerous. Please, keep away." The children had been playing rounders, when Jane hit the ball so hard, that it went across the field, and over the railings. Jane knew that no-one was allowed inside the railings. What were they to do?

Ginger Gregg was a good climber, but he was very small. He volunteered to go over the railings, to get the ball, if some of the children would lift him up on their shoulders. Ginger climbed on to Jane's shoulders, and he was soon over the railings. He dropped inside the area of the railings. He threw the ball back over the top of the high railings. Then to his horror, because there were no children inside the railings to lift him up, he could not get out again. The railings were so high, and sharp.

"Get me out of here. Get me out of here," Ginger was shouting at the top of his voice. The other children were shouting too, "Ginger cannot get back over the railings." Some others just smiled, and looked at the predicament, that Ginger had got himself into. No doubt, Ginger was caught, as if he were in a cage.

"We shall have to 'phone for the fire-brigade," Jane said. The police always follow the fire-engines. We are going to be caught and arrested. We are in a pickle now!' Jane and Ginger were beginning to feel panic. The young Baptist Minister happened to be passing in his car, just at that moment. He stopped to find out what was wrong. Ginger kept shouting out through the railings, "Get me out. Get me out of here."

Ladies from the houses over the street, came over to see what had happened. The dustmen stopped their truck, to look at Ginger shouting from behind the railings. The newspaper reporter came over to get information for the local newspaper. Olive the newspaper photographer was taking photographs of the event. The milkman driving his milk-van stopped to ask Ginger if he would like a bottle of milk to drink.

Mr. Boots the Policeman arrived, and began to write something in his note-book. Nurse McGreggor stopped, getting off her bicycle, holding her little black bag, which she always carried. She said that she was sorry that could not help. The crowd of people was increasing all the time, because even more school children were arriving.

Ginger was getting really frightened, by this time. The window cleaner, was up on his ladder, cleaning the windows at house number forty-two. He wondered what all the fuss was about, so he slung his ladder over his shoulder, and came over to see that Ginger was stuck inside the railings. He put his ladders against the railings, and, ran up the ladder, and jumped inside the railings to land on his feet, down beside Ginger. The people all cheered. Jane, the children, the Baptist minister, the dustmen, the newspaper reporter, the photographer, the policeman, the nurse, and all the other school children all clapped their hands and cheered.

The window cleaner said to Ginger, "Now there are two cheeky monkeys inside the cage for all to see." Ginger began to see the funny side of things and he started to giggle. Then, before anyone could say "Jack Robinson", the window cleaner had brought his ladder inside the railings. He hoisted Ginger over his shoulder, and quickly ran up his ladder, He jumped to the ground outside. Ginger was free again! The window cleaner put his ladder over his shoulder. He gave Ginger a wink, and a cheery "Goodbye. All is well that ends well,!" Off he went to clean the windows further down the street. Ginger and the school children shouted to him, "Thank You very much." Jane, Ginger, and the other children never went near the Gas pumping station again.

Now for the seven questions. 1. Was Ginger disobedient? 2. Did Ginger think *before* he went after the ball? 3. Why were the people so helpless? 4. Why was the window-cleaner so successful? 5. Why did the crowd gather? 6. What should they have done, if there had been no window cleaner with ladders about at that time? What private lesson have you learned from this story?

Prayer:

> Heavenly Father show us how to keep away from danger.
> Teach us to look, before we leap in life.
> We thank you for people who help us.
> We thank you for Jesus, who came to be our friend.
> We pray for any boy or girl in trouble.
> Make us wise, kind and honest at all times.   Amen.

Hymn:

> When the saints go marching in. (JP. 195),
> or, We are climbing Jesus' ladder. (C&P.1. 49)

Teachers' Note:(1) High railings are dangerous places for children to try to climb. (2) Always look before you leap in life. (Use thinking time in your own mind). (3) You may always find a good friend, somewhere, who can help you.

(c) Poisonous Snakes

Week 6   Danger.

When the Israelites were making their journey through the Desert, they were like a large army, but instead of being only soldiers, they were really a large army of women, men, and children. They were both young and old people among them. There were under the leadership of Moses, travelling to the promised land. God had made a promise to his people that he would give them a new land to inhabit, after they had escaped from Egypt.

The journey took about forty years to walk, and often the people became unhappy with the difficulties of the journey. Sometimes they were short of water.

Often they were tired and exhausted. Sometimes they longed to go back to Egypt, even though they had suffered much and even though they had been slaves there.

They spoke against God and against Moses. They said, "Why have you brought us out of Egypt, to die in this Desert. There is no bread here, and little water, and we have become tired of the Manna, which we have to eat every day." (Manna was a small white substance which fell with the dew, that they gathered each morning, just as in Britain mushrooms grow up in the night.)

After all their grumbling against God and their Leader, Moses, they travelled to a place, which was very dangerous. There were many poisonous snakes crawling about. The people believed that God had sent the snakes among them, because they had been grumbling. The poisonous snakes bit many of the people, and they began to die.

The Israelite people came to Moses, and said to him, "We have sinned against God by our complaining so much. We are sorry that we have spoken against you our Leader. Please, pray to the Lord for us, and ask him to take away these poisonous snakes from amongst us." Moses loved the Israelite people, so he prayed to the Lord, and asked for help.

The Lord answered his prayer. He told Moses to make a snake, (a pretend one, not a real one) and to put it upon a pole. Anyone who looked at the man-made snake, after they had been bitten, would not die. They would recover from their snake-bite. Soon, Moses made a bronze (similar to brass) snake, and he fixed it to a pole in the middle of the camp.

True enough, everyone who looked at the bronze snake, after they had suffered snake-bite, was cured immediately. After that time, no one else died of snake-bite. There was a mysterious healing power in looking at the snake on the pole. The Israelite people kept on walking over the sandy hills of the desert, until they eventually reached the Promised Land. They settled down in the Promised Land, and they made it their own homeland. They built houses, farms and towns, and lived together in happiness.

In St. John's Gospel, (written about 100 years A.D.) the author tells us that Jesus once referred to the bronze snake. Here is what Jesus said. "As Moses lifted up the bronze snake in the Desert, even so must the Son of Man be lifted up, that that everyone who believes in him, may have eternal life." These words mean that Jesus died upon a cross, that we all might have eternal life through believing in him. Believing is like a look of faith.

Mrs. Cecil Francis Alexander's, (1818-95), beautiful Irish hymn says,

> There is a green hill far away,
> outside a city wall.
> Were the dear Lord was crucified,
> Who died to save us all.

We may not know, we cannot tell,
What pains he had to bear.
But we believe it was for us,
He hung and suffered there.

Prayer:

Heavenly Father, we thank you for the story
of the healing power of the bronze snake
in the desert.
We also thank you,
that because Jesus died on the cross,
we may find new spiritual life,
by believing in him.   Amen.

Hymn:

There is a green hill far away. (JP. 245),
or, At the name of Jesus. (C&P.1. 58), (JP. 13)

Teachers' Note: (1) Sometimes, children grumble, when they should be thankful.
(2) There is a symbolism (explain the symbolism of the pole, which John's
Gospel interprets as being like the cross) in the Old Testament story of the bronze
snake. (John 3 verse 14). There is spiritual healing (forgiveness) in the cross. (3)
God is the God of forgiveness. Reference Numbers 21; 4-8.

(a) **The Red-hot Coal**   *Week 7   The Church Family*

*Since, we have had clean air laws, and smokeless zones in our towns, we do
not see many household fireplaces which use coal as a fuel. The chimneys do not
belch smoke nowadays. One single fire burning coal, causes smoke to come out of
the house chimney. A street of houses burning coal, causes such a lot of smoke to
go into the air. So you can guess how much smoke comes from the chimneys of a
whole town. Smoke poisons the air, and people who breathe in the poisoned air,
may suffer from asthma or other chest illnesses. When households use gas or
electric heating, it helps to keep the air clean from pollution.*

Our story belongs to the times when every house burned coal in their fireplaces. The was once a good man, by the name of "old Bob" who worked about a
country church. Bob was a steward, (a church official who does various duties,
such as giving out hymnbooks, or keeping account of church funds). He also kept
the church clean and tidy. He cut the grass in the grave-yard. He did all the odd
jobs about the church, free of charge. He liked to think that in this way, he was
serving the Lord, and also helping other people at the same time. Then some

foolish members of the church talked behind the old Bob's back. They said that he did not keep the pews in the church, as clean as they used to be.

This gossip really hurt old Bob, and he went on the huff. He said,to himself, "Well, if that is all they think of my hard work for the church, for these twenty years, then I shall resign. I will not attend church again! The members do not appreciate my help." So old Bob did not come to the Services at the church anymore.

Now the Minister Priest at the church, really appreciated old Bob's work in the past. Old Bob had helped him out, cleaning up after the Harvest Festival. He had always put up the Christmas tree in the church each year, and he took it away again afterwards, and cleaned the floor. The Minister was sorry that old Bob had been hurt by the gossip, because he knew old Bob very well, indeed.

The Minister called at old Bob's cottage, and old Bob felt a little embarrassed, as he invited the minister in. Both men sat on arm-chairs, and watched the big coal fire burning brightly. Neither the Minister, nor Bob said a word. Then the Minister took the brass tongs in his hand.

He lifted a red hot coal from the middle of the blazing fire, and put it upon the stone hearth. Both men watched the blazing red-hot coal burn brightly. Neither of them spoke. They watched the red-hot coal, until after about fifteen minutes, the flame went out, and the single piece of coal, went grey and black, as the coal became cooler, and cooler. The flame had gone. The warmth had gone. Only a piece of grey ash remained.

Still, the Minister never said a word, as old Bob and he watched the ash on the hearth. Old Bob realised that the Minister was preaching a sermon to him, when he took the red hot coal out from among the other coals in the fire. He thought to himself, the fire is the church congregation, and I am the blazing coal. I have come away from the church. Once I was red-hot and eager to help the church. Now I have lost the flame of love in my heart. I am growing cold-hearted every day I stay away from church.

The Minister, smiled at old Bob, and both men never spoke, as the Minister rose to leave. In silence, old Bob had received the message from the parable of the flaming coal. He understood! Next Sunday, Old Bob was back at church again. He sat in his usual pew at the back. He was such a happy man now, for he had to admit, that he loved the church, and while he had stayed way, he had been very unhappy inside himself.

"I will never be a dying coal again, he said to himself" "I shall never let my red hot enthusiasm for the Lord's work, ever go out again. I shall keep close to all the other red hot coals. Every church family is like a fire that welcomes someone else." Old Bob never missed attending the fellowship of the church again! Do you know what the old saying means, "Birds of a feather, stay together?"

Prayer:

> Heavenly Father, we thank you for the friendship
> and fellowship of Christian friends.
> We thank you for all that we learn,
> as we worship in our school assembly.
> Bless our teachers, and any pupils
> who are absent today.   Amen.

Hymn:

Colours of day dawn into my mind. (C&P.1. 55), (JP. 28)

Teachers' Note: (1) Fellowship means genuine friendship. Unkind gossip may break up a group of school friends. (2) We must learn to discipline our tongues, by not saying unkind words about others. (3) Old Bob realised that he needed the church, just as much as the church needed him. The opening paragraph is necessary, because many children, nowadays, have never seen a real coal fire.

(b) The Princess Victoria   *Week 7   The Church Family*

During the 1950's a beautiful ship was built, named the "Princess Victoria." She was a large ferry boat, which carried lorries, cars, and heavy goods, from Stranraer in Scotland to Larne in Ireland. Back and forth she sailed. She had a very good Captain, named Captain Ferguson. She also had a very good crew.

Now, to get the lorries, cars, caravans, and even buses, on to the boat, two great steel doors were opened in the stern of the ship. A steel gangway from the inside the ship was laid down to reach the quayside. It was a simple idea, and all the motor vehicles easily drove up the steel gangway, to come to a halt inside a vast garage below deck. The cars and buses and caravans lined up beside each other. Their drivers could enjoy a meal in the cafe higher up on the decks.

The Princess Victoria sailed out one dark stormy night to cross the Irish Sea to Larne. Usually the journey took about two hours. On this night when the ship was half way across the sea, the storm became very fierce. The waves rose up like mountains as they struck the ship. After the storm had battered the ship for a some time, the sea broke open the great steel doors in the stern. The brave crewmen tried get the sea-doors to shut again, but they could not keep the water out. Eventually the sea rushed inside, and filled the large garage inside the ship, where the lorries and cars were stored.

Captain Ferguson realised that his ship was sinking. He immediately tried to steer the Princess Victoria towards the shelter of Belfast Lough. The force of the storm carried the ship Southwards. There were other ships nearby which could have been sent from either the mainland or from Ireland to help. Unfortunately, there was no "ship to shore telephone" installed in the huge ferry.

This meant that the ship could not communicate with people on the shore. It had not been realised apparently, just how important it was to maintain good communication. Tragically, the ship sank slowly, ever so slowly, until it disappeared beneath the cold icy sea. Only a few passengers and crew were saved. Most people were drowned in the storm, including the Captain.

Now, for second tale about a Bible storm. Jesus had been telling stories which he called "parables". The various stories were about oil lamps, and about sowing seeds, and about the tiny mustard seed. Crowds gathered around him to hear him speak. He had been holding discussions with the people for most of the day. As the evening drew near, he felt very tired. He said to his disciples, "Let us join the other boats, and go for a sail across the lake, to the shore on the far side of the lake."

So they left the crowd behind them. They sailed in a small fishing boat across the water. As they sailed over the waves, the rhythm of the waves lapping on the side of the boat, helped Jesus to close his eyes, and to fall asleep in the stern of the boat. Jesus was very tired. He rested his head on a cushion.

As Jesus was asleep, the disciples guided the steering rudder, and kept the sails in the correct position. Half way over, they ran into a storm. These storms often came very suddenly on the lake. The waves came over the side into the boat, and the boat was nearly swamped. Some of the disciples were expert fishermen. As the storm became worse, the disciples, despite being experts, they became afraid.

Realising that at sea, communication was very important, the disciples awakened Jesus from his sleep. They called out to him, "Master, do you not care if we drown?" Jesus woke up. He clearly saw the dangerous position they were in. To their amazement, he stood up, and rebuked the wind. "Be quiet. Peace be still," he said. Then, the storm began to die down, and the sea became calm again

Jesus said to his disciples, "Why are you so much afraid? Have you not any faith?" The men were terrified. They said to each other, "Who is this man? Even the wind and the waves obey him." Soon, they had reached the other side of the lake, and they were safe on the shore again.

Christians still communicate with Jesus through the act of prayer. Let us pray now for all who face the danger of the sea. A ship's crew are like members of one family.

Prayer:

>   Father God, we thank you
>   that Jesus was not afraid of the storm.
>   We ask you to bless all those who sail the seas.

Guard them, and bring them home
safely to their families again.
Teach us that praying to God,
is a form of communication.   Amen.

Hymn:

In the morning early, I go down to the sea. (C&P.1. 60),
or, Waves are beating on the shore. (C&P.2. 84)

Teachers' Note: (1) Everyone knows fear at some time. (2) The disciples could communicate with Jesus. (3) We owe gratitude to crews who sail the seas.

(c) The Epileptic Boy   *Week 7   The Church Family*

A man came near to Jesus, and he knelt down before him. He said, "Jesus have pity on my boy, and help him. My boy has seizures, (Epileptic fits) and it makes him very ill. When he has a seizure, he falls down to the ground. Sometimes, he may fall into the fire, or into water, depending where he is standing at that moment. I brought my boy to your disciples, but they could not heal him, nor help him."

Jesus said to the father of the boy, who believed that a demon must be inside the lad, making him so ill. "Bring the boy to me" The father brought his boy to Jesus. Then, Jesus rebuked the demon, and instantly, it left the boy. Jesus performed a miracle, and from that time onwards, the boy was cured. He had his normal health restored to him. He became just like any other child in the street. He never again fell down on the ground, or into the fire, or into a well. It was a real cure!

The disciples asked Jesus, "Why could we not heal the boy, and drive out the demon?" Jesus replied, "You could not help the boy, because your faith is so small. If you had faith, as small as a tiny mustard seed, you could say to this mountain, move from here to there, and it would happen." (A grain of mustard seed is as small as a speck of pepper). Jesus believed that faith in God, could solve any problem.

Nowadays, because we have hospitals, with highly trained Doctors and Nurses, who use X-rays, and scanners, to study our bodies, they can treat, and even cure diseases with special medicines. As Christians, we need to be well educated, and informed about sickness.

If anyone has epilepsy in your school, you must not think that he or she has been a bad person. Many illnesses are with us before we were born. Doctors and Nurses do the work of God in our life-time, when they perform operations, and bring healing to their patients. We must always pray for the great work of healing that goes on all around us.

When Marion, aged ten, fell off a wall, on to which she had climbed. She cried a lot, because of her pain. The x-ray negative looked like a dark photograph, and it showed that Marion's lower left leg had been broken. The Doctors bandaged the leg up tight. Then, a technician was called, and he put a soaking wet plaster of paris, just like white cement, all round her bandages. The plaster of paris, hardened almost immediately. Marion had to walk about, and attend school, with her stiff white leg, which was as white as the ceiling. She allowed some children to write their names on her plaster.

Someone wrote, "Humpty Dumpty" on her knee. Can you guess why? In six weeks time, the same man at the hospital, cut the plaster of paris off He used a little electric saw, cutting-machine. The plaster of paris peeled off, like a leg-shaped shell.

Next, a lady physio-therapist showed Marion how to walk normally again. At first, she kept falling down, just like the boy in the Bible story. She found that her muscles had stiffened up. The lady made her walk, and she showed Marion, how to bend her knee, even though it was very painful to do so. "What we do not use, we lose the power over," the lady physio-therapist explained. When Marion went back to school, her friends shouted across the play-ground, "Marion, it is lovely to see you back at school again!"

Prayer:

> Heavenly Father, we pray for all children
> who lie ill in hospital.
> We pray also, for any handicapped children.
> Bless and guide doctors and nurses,
> and ambulance workers,
> in the good work of healing.
> We thank you for Jesus, the great healer.   Amen.

Hymn:

> I will bring you the best gift I can offer. (C&P.1. 55),
> or, The wise may bring their learning. (C&P.1. 64), (JP. 253)

Teachers' Note: Allow the pupils to raise questions. (1) This lesson is meant to teach that sickness is not generally caused by personal wrong-doing. (accidents). (2) It is meant to show the link between the healing of Jesus, and present day medical science. (3) We need to appreciate the daily good work of hospitals.

(a) The Muslim Boy

Ali was a Muslim boy, whose father and mother had come to England from India. Ali's parents had worked hard, saved money, and they had bought an English house. They attended the local Mosque. They were very happy to live in Britain.

Ali their first son, had been born in England, so he considered himself to be as English as anyone else who had been born in England. He loved the school which he attended, because he was a bright boy, and he wanted to learn. The Head-teacher, and some of the children, asked Ali to tell them about his being a Muslim.

Ali told them that their family religion lived by a Holy Book called the Quor'an. He told the children, that his father attended the Mosque on a Friday. The Mosque had no images in it, nor had it any pictures. Instead, on the walls of the Mosque were painted beautiful patterns. Sometimes these wall patterns were based on geometric shapes.

Sometimes the patterns were plant shapes. Sometimes the painted shapes on the wall came from Arabic writings. However, there were no pictures of human beings or animals in the Mosque. Ali said that the Prophet Muhammad, their spiritual guide, had been born in the year A.D. 570.

Ali explained that their whole Islamic faith is summed up in the Arabic language, in the words of the *Shahada,* which is the declaration of their faith. It means, *"There is no God but Allah (Arabic for "God"), and Muhammad is the messenger of God."* He explained that the meaning of the word "Islam" is "submission." Every Muslim submits himself or herself, to the will of the one true God. The word, "God" in the Arabic language is, "Allah."

Ali explained that Muslims prayed five times every day. Many Muslims own a Prayer mat, for kneeling in order to worship God. Ali, further explained, to the children that there was an ancient holy building overseas in the city of Meccah (Saudi Arabia) called the "Kaba". Muslims believe that Ibrahim (Hebrew Abraham) and his son, Ishmael built the Kaba long ago. While they are in the Mosque, the worshippers of Allah, know the direction of Mekkah, because there is a niche mark on the Mosque wall, which points in that direction. The congregation always pray towards Mekkah. The Immam usually preaches from a pulpit in the Mosque on a Friday.

Ali was very good at describing his religion. He said that Muslims pray with their faces bowed towards the ground. Before prayer, Muslims wash themselves carefully, hands, arms, face, head, legs, and feet. In this way they show respect for Allah (God). For this reason, every Mosque has a washing area.

Ali explained that Muslims were not just Muslims at the Mosque. Muslims try to practise their religion every hour of the day. They also keep a special period of celebrations during the Muslim month of Ramadam. **The most important belief that Muslims hold, is that God is ONE God.** *(Looking at this statement from the Christian viewpoint, Muslims do not have a doctrine of the "Trinity." That God is Father, Son and Holy Spirit.)*

When Ali had finished telling his school friends about his faith, the children were very grateful, indeed. They had learnt as much from Ali, as they had from the Teacher that day.

Prayer:

> Hear us, O Lord, our one God.
> We thank you for our health and strength.
> We thank you for our minds and spirits.
> We thank you for families and schools.
> We thank you that God loves
> children of all religions.   Amen.

Hymn:

> Let us with a gladsome mind. (C&P.1. 8), (JP. 154)

Teachers' Note: (1) Notice that the boy Ali belonged to a religious community known as "Islam". (2) Notice that the boy Ali had a personal faith in Allah (God). (3) Notice that Ali knew that he must practise his faith in the world outside the Mosque.

(b) More about the Muslim Boy

Week 8   Muslims

Next morning at the School Assembly, the Head teacher asked Ali, if he would tell the children some more about his religion. "Tell us about the Mineret," he asked him. Ali explained that the Mineret was high tower outside the Mosque, from which the faithful Muslims are called to prayer by a "Caller". Just as Churches in Britain use bells to call people to the church services, so the Caller stands high up in the Mineret, and he calls out through a window, at the top of his voice, in the Arabic Language.

He shouts: "Allah is most great. I bear witness that there is no God but Allah: I bear witness that Muhammad is Allah's messenger. Hurry to prayer. Hurry to success. Allah is most great. There is no God but Allah. Muhammad is Allah's Messenger."

Ali explained that Muslims do not drink alcholic drinks, because they believe that such drinks make people forget God. They do not eat any part of a pig, which they consider to be an unclean animal. So, Muslims never eat pork.

Ali explained that Muslims are very modest in how they dress. Women must cover their bodies, except for arms and legs. Men must always be covered from the navel to the knees. Every Mosque has a large prayer room for the men to unite in prayer. There may be another room, or a screened-off area in the Mosque for the Muslim women, because women and men worship apart. Muslims are very reverent in worshipping Allah. They bow themselves to the ground in their prayers. They remove their shoes before going into the Mosque. Every Mosque has a washing area for the worshippers. Muslims like to be clean, before they say their prayers.

Finally, Ali came to the end of this talk about his faith. He said that his father had told him, that there were 13,000 million Muslims around the world today. The children, and the head-teacher thanked Ali for his clear explanation of the Islamic faith.

Prayer:

> Heavenly Father, we pray for needy people
> in our own country.
> We ask for the spirit of tolerance
> towards other children and their relations
> who may worship differently from ourselves.
> We owe you our thanks, Lord, for your goodness to us all.
> Make us all contented people.   Amen.

Hymn:

> Praise to the Lord, the Almighty, (C&P.1. 34)

Teachers Note: (1) The Holy Book, the Quor'an is written in Arabic. (2) There is much more detail that Ali had yet to learn about his religion. Religion is about a life long practice. (3) We ought to respect the faith of other people in God.

(c) Ali's Sermon   *Week 8   Muslims*

For the third morning, the Headteacher asked Ali to tell the class something more about the Muslim religion. Ali by this time had lost his fear of speaking to all the children in the Assembly. He said to them, "I feel like as if I am an Immam, preaching from his pulpit in the Mosque, on Friday morning. Of course, I do not know as much as the older Muslims, but I will share with you what I know."

Ali said, "Sometimes we may see a large building, being held up by stone pillars. These pillars keep the building strong and secure. The Muslim religion also has what are called the "Five Pillars of Islam". These five pillars keep our religion strong in our hearts and minds, wherever we may live. Here they are:

Muslims do not eat in the month of Ramadam during the hours of daylight.

Muslims pray five times every day.

Muslims believe that there is one God, and that Muhammad was his prophet.

Muslims give Zakat money to charity or to the needy people.

Muslims try to visit the holy Kaba in Makkah, at least once in their life-time.

So you will not forget if I tell you, that Muslims keep their holy day on a Friday. The Jews keep their Sabbath on a Saturday. Christians keep their holy day on a Sunday."

"Just as the symbolic sign of the Jews is the six-pointed star of David, and the sign of Christians is the cross, so the symbolic sign of Muslims is the "Crescent Moon, with a star in the middle of it." So Ali ended his three talks about his Islamic faith. The Headteacher and the children thanked him for the excellent manner he had made everything so clear.

Prayer:

> Heavenly Father,
> We pray for all children of world religions.
> We pray also for hungry children overseas.
> We remember children whose home-lands,
> are still disturbed by war.
> Lord, may peace be all over our world.   Amen.

Hymn:

> Kum ba ya, my Lord, kum ba ya. (C&P.1. 68), (JP. 149)

Teachers' Note: (1) The Five Pillars of Islam are a summing up of the Muslim religion. (2) Have you noticed how the three religions, the faith of the Jews, and the faith of Christians, and the faith of Muslims all came from the Near Eastern countries? (3) Have you noticed that the three religions all believe in the same God? They are similar in some respects, yet very different in others.

(a) St. Patrick's Day

Monica was a little Irish-American girl, aged ten, who lived with her Mother on the fifteenth floor of a New York Sky-scraper building. That may seem to be a high building, but in New York there are many much higher buildings than that. Monica and her Mum never walked up the stairs, they always used the elevators.

The year came round to St. Patrick's day. Monica and her Mother went to see the Great St. Patrick's Day parade marching down Broadway. Mother told Monica that if ever she was lost, and there was no policeman about, to go into the open door of a church. You may always feel safe to tell the Priest or Minister.

On this particular day, the crowds thronged the pavements, and sidewalks. People were wearing green shamrocks, and green hats, and green uniforms. Everyone was very happy, as the parade passed down Broadway. The bands played their Irish music, and marching girls danced like trumpet majors all over the middle of the road. Clerks in offices very high up in the buildings were letting ticker-tape (long pieces of cut paper from office machines) fall like white snow, on the people below in the street.

People were laughing, and walking with their arms linked together. It was just then, that little Monica became lost in the crowd. She found herself being swept along with the people, and just for a moment, she had let go of her mother's hand. Her mum had vanished. She became frightened among so many strangers. She thought that she might be carried along with the laughing crowd, right up to Central Park. So she looked upwards, and she saw the Spire of St. Patrick's Cathedral.

Monica made her way towards the Cathedral, walking along beside the buildings and the rushing crowd. At last she reached the Cathedral. She slipped inside the big front door. She made her way up the aisle to the front of the church. There was a chair beside the Grotto, (a place for praying), which held a sculpture of Jesus on the cross. Monica thought to herself, if I sit near Jesus on the cross, I will be quite safe. Inside the Cathedral, there were hundreds of seats, so there was room for anyone else, who was lost.

After Monica sat for about half an hour, a gentleman dressed in black, green, and gold, came into the Cathedral to say a prayer beside the Grotto of the Cross of Jesus. He had not noticed her because he was praying silently. He had a kind face. When at last he opened his eyes, he looked at little Monica. "Are you all alone, little girl," he asked. Monica replied, "Yes. I am lost. My Mum says that I have always to tell a policeman, or go to Church, if I ever get lost."

The gentleman dressed in black, green and gold was non other, than the Mayor of New York himself. Monica became excited, when he took a radio telephone out of his pocket. He said, "I'll call the Bishop, he will know just what to do."

The Bishop came rushing into the Cathedral, a few moments after he had been called by the Mayor. He spoke ever so kindly, "My child, so you have been lost at the St. Patrick's Day Parade. What is you full name, and I will put an announcement over the Local Radio system." Monica told him her full name, because there could be many Monica O'Farrells in New York on St. Patrick's day.

They went to the door of the Cathedral, and she heard the amplifier announcing to the public, "Will the mother of Monica, Kathleen, Teresa, O'Farrell please come to the front door of the Cathedral to find her lost daughter. Thank you!" The policemen were calling out to people around, "Will the mother of Monica, Kathleen, Teresa, O'Farrell, come to the Cathedral front door. Please!"

Monica thought, "This is exciting! The Mayor of New York, and the Catholic Bishop, and the policemen, are interested in taking care of me." Soon, Mum came rushing up to the Cathedral, and gathered Monica into her arms. The Mayor gave her a beautiful green and red doll, a little Irish Colleen, which was the popular image of an Irish country girl. The Mayor said that the doll had been made in Ireland.

The Bishop smiled and he gave her a little Church medal, and a plant of real Irish Shamrock, which had just been flown into New York that morning. "Plant it in a window box, it will grow in America too," he whispered. A New York Policeman gave her a beautiful little handkerchief, with Ireland embroidered upon it. Everyone that day seemed to be connected with Ireland.

Monica and her Mum safely went home, back into the elevator, up to her flat on the fifteenth floor. They had had a wonderfully exciting day. However, Monica never wanted to be lost again! She gave her Mum a big hug. "North, South, East and West, home is best." Monica sang, back in her own room.

Monica remembered the story which Jesus told, about the shepherd with the hundred sheep. One sheep became lost on the hillside. The good shepherd left the others in the sheep-fold, and searched until he found the lost sheep. He carried the lost sheep on his shoulder back to the safety of the fold. He was full of joy, and so was Monica's Mum.

Prayer:

> Lord we thank you for happy times.
> We pray for any child who may feel lost
> or alone.
> Teach us that God is our true friend.
> Show us that Jesus is the Good Shepherd.
> We pray for lonely children.   Amen.

Hymn:

> The bell of creation is swinging for ever. (C&P.1. 86),
> or, Amazing grace! How sweet the sound. (JP. 8)

Teachers' Note: (1) New York St. Patrick's Day Parade is a crowded occasion. It is held on the 17th. March each year. (2) A child may become lost in the crowd. (3) Better never to be lost! Hold your parent's hand.

(b) Robin finds a Friend

Week 9   Lost and Found

There is a legend that Robin Hood and his merry men were a band of robbers who lived in Sherwood Forest, near the city of Nottingham. Sir Robin Lockesly had been robbed of the ownership of his castle and lands. He took to the woods, and lived his life out among the forest, with Maid Marion, the lady he loved. His band of merry men used to hunt the King's deer. They ate the deer, which they had cooked on great fires. They loved the smell of venison. It is said that they robbed the rich, and gave it to the poor.

His men had many strange names, such as Will Scarlet, Robin the Miller, Little John, and most famous of all, was Friar Tuck. Robin hood was their leader, and they would always obey his orders. One day, Friar Tuck, who had not yet joined Robin Hood's merry men, was travelling through the forest alone. He was rather a fat Friar, (a Monk), because he liked to eat a lot. He was a good man of God. He could defend himself, if he had to, against robbers. He always carried about with him, a quarter-staff (a thick round pole made of oak-wood).

On his journey through the forest he came to a river, which had a log cut down over the water to serve as a bridge. Friar Tuck was walking across the log, when he was confronted by Robin Hood crossing the river from the other side. "Robin said, "Here now, Holy Monk, you had better step aside, and let me across the log -bridge." Friar Tuck replied, "I am more than half-way over the log-bridge, you had better let me pass."

Robin Hood was almost a perfect shot with his bow and arrow. He could also defend himself with a broad-sword. He was not afraid of Friar Tuck. Friar Tuck only liked to use his quarter-staff because he was not really a man of war, but of peace. The good Friar was stubborn and refused to move out of the way, and Robin Hood also was stubborn and he refused to stand aside on the log bridge.

They decided to fight it out. Robin saw that all his merry men were watching him, so he took a quarter-staff, which was longer than a brush shaft. Both men began to fight. The fight continued in earnest, when Friar Tuck hit Robin Hood a blow on the arm and then a blow on the side. Robin, fought back, and he hit the good friar on the rump, and nearly knocked him into the river.

Friar Tuck was smiling all the time, and teasing Robin as he fought him. "Come on, you can do better than that, he was saying," as he hit Robin with the staff. Then with a twinkle in his eye, he said, "Here, Sir Robin, I have had enough of your obstruction." As quick as lightening, Friar Tuck hit Robin with his staff on the shoulder, and then he used the bottom of his staff to entangle in between Robin's ankles. He lifted Robin into the air, and threw him into the middle of the water. He laughed to himself and walked slowly over the log-bridge. He stretched his quarter-staff out to Robin, who was swimming in the river. Robin was laughing too, as Friar Tuck pulled him into the river bank safely. They both enjoyed the joke.

Friar Tuck said to Robin Hood, "You did not need to be so stubborn, and make me throw you into the river." Robin Hood laughed, and said, "Yes. Pride goes before a fall." Friar Tuck and Robin Hood became the best of friends, and the merry men welcomed him to join Robin's men of Sherwood forest. In those days the band of Robin's merry men really needed a minister of religion, because they had no church in the forest. One day, Maid Marion would need someone to marry her to Robin Hood. Friar Tuck was a useful friend to have!

Prayer:

> Father God, we thank you for the old stories,
> of the past, which we enjoy.
> Teach us not to be stubborn,
> when we could make good friends,
> by being courteous, and reasonable.
> Bring peace into every part of the world.   Amen.

Hymn:

> When a knight won his spurs in the stories of old. (C&P.1. 50)

Teachers' Note: (1) Both men refused to give way in this story. (2) How easy it would have been to make a "compromise." (3) Someone has said, "Win an argument, and lose a friend." Sometimes is is wiser not to pursue an argument, and in that way, keep a friendship.

(c) The Older Brother   *Week 9   Lost and Found*

When Jesus told the story of the prodigal son, he also mentioned a second older brother. ("Prodigal" means a wasteful person). The younger prodigal son had taken the money belonging to him, and that he had left home, for the far country. Away from home, he had wasted his money in foolish living. His friends had all left him, now that his money had been used up. The only job that he could get, was working on a pig farm. He was hungry so often, that he could have eaten the food that the pigs were eating. Finally, the prodigal son came back home, and he was welcomed by his Father, who made a feast for him.

Now, there was an older brother in the family, who worked very hard on his Father's farm. He did not run away, and leave his Father in the lurch. He did not waste his Father's money. He just worked on at the farm. Imagine his surprise, when coming back from the fields, he heard of feasting and music in the big barn. A servant told the older brother, that the younger son had come home, after having squandered everything he owned. He was starving and hungry. His Father was so pleased to see him again, that he had run to greet him.

The older brother was very angry, because his Father had made such a hearty meal, on the return of the wandering boy. He was angry at the rejoicing, and all the fuss being made. He stood outside the party in the barn, and refused to go inside. He thought of his younger brother as a wastrel, not worth bothering about.

The Father came out of the celebrations, and they talked outside. The older brother said, "Why are you killing the fatted calf, and setting out a regular feast, Dad? All these years have I worked for you here on the farm, and you did not as much as kill a young goat to give me a special meal, with my friends. Yet here is your son, (notice that he did not say, "here is my brother".) Here is your son, who has wasted and squandered all the money which you gave him, arriving back here, smelling of pigs, and penniless. Yet you give him a "Welcome Party" and a first class meal.

The Father answered the older brother, "Son everything I own on the farm will become yours. We had to make a celebration in the big barn, because it is your brother who was dead and is alive again. He was lost and is found. The older brother did not welcome his younger brother home again, because he was jealous of all the attention his younger brother was receiving. The older brother was on the huff. He lacked forgiveness and generosity.

Jesus told the story about the TWO SONS. Which one do you think the Father loved the most. A good parent loves all his children the same, even though they may be different in character. The younger son had many obvious faults. The older son had many hidden hateful thoughts. One was wasteful, and careless out among people in the world. The other was spiteful, resentful, unforgiving and proud, deep down in his heart.

Jesus told the story to explain that the older son was just as bad as the younger son, because he could not forgive his brother. The younger son was sorry for all his foolish past way of life. There are many people who have made wrong choices in life who come back to the Church of Jesus Christ. We must also remember there are many very good people out in the everyday world, who may not attend Church very often. God really loves them all.

Prayer:

> Lord of the whole earth, Lord of people,
> and Lord of little children,
> Teach us to be forgiving and kind.
> Cleanse from our hearts,
> any hatred, malice, or envy.
> Bless foolish people, and reward wise people.
> In your mercy, forgive us all.   Amen.

Hymn:

> Lord of all hopefulness, Lord of all joy. (C&P.1. 52), (JP. 157)

Teachers' Note: (1) Some people act in a foolish manner, and waste their own lives. (2) Some people try to be upright, and to believe in Jesus. (3) God, because he is God, loves everyone, both good and bad. His love and grace enables us all to change our ways for the better. God may love the sinner, but hate his sin. Reference St. Luke Chapter 15.verses 25-32.

(a) The Stand-in

Week 10   Dependable people

Helen was a good singer, and she wanted to sing in the school play. However, Mrs. Grainger, the school Drama teacher, came to Helen, and she asked her a private question. "Helen, I know that you are a good singer, but as a favour, I would like to ask you to be a "Stand-in" for Louise Wilson, in the school play. Would you also mind doubling up both as a Stand-in, and also as a Deputy, for the solo part in the last choir piece. I mean the Final Chorale."

Helen dearly wanted to sing a solo part in the school play, and here the Teacher was asking her to simply be a second best. They wanted her to be someone to fall back on, to use if they needed her. Helen felt hurt inside. She went home to her mother, and told her what she had been asked to do. "They must not think much of me," she said. "I am not number one, I am only number two."

Helen's mother listened thoughtfully. "Did the Drama Teacher ask anyone else to do a special part?" "No,"· Mum, she said. "Everyone was given a part in the Play. Teacher said, that I was to learn as many of the other girls' and boys' parts as I could." Mum phoned up Mrs. Grainger at the school, to talk about the problem. "Mrs. Grainger, said that Helen had the best voice, and the best memory in the upper school. She had been specially chosen to do a very difficult part. They were trying to raise money for the Childrens' Hospice, so the school play had to be extra well produced. Please, ask Helen to do what I asked her to do."

Next day, Helen met the Drama Teacher with a smile, and she agreed to be a substitute on the big night of the play, which was to be held in the local theatre. Helen never did much in the practice sessions, instead she had to listen to everyone else saying and singing their parts. The practising went on for six weeks. Helen noticed that the Drama Teacher was treating her, as if she were an adult. It was as if she were another teacher.

On the evening of the presentation of the Play, a disaster struck. Louise Wilson had a sore throat, and her mother said that she could not sing a note. She was hoarse. Mrs. Grainger just smiled, and said that was quite all right. She said that she had made preparations for such an emergency.

She rushed round to the dressing rooms, and she whispered to Helen. "Quickly now, put on the Princess' golden and silver dress, with the stars all over it. You wear her diamond crown. Put her rings on your fingers. You will have to be her substitute to-night. Louise Wilson cannot sing a note. She is ill at home."

Helen rushed to get into the silver and gold dress. The ladies combed out her hair, and painted her nails. Then, at the proper place, all the children gathered in the Royal Hall, on stage, and they began to sing as a choir. Helen appeared on the stage, as the Princess, and she sang the beautiful song, "I am a little Princess, and I'll soon be a Queen." Helen had not used her voice very much during the previous two weeks. It was in beautiful sweet and strong condition.

Helen sang like a nightingale. She was terrific! She never had to use a music book, because she had the song in her mind, and heart. Everyone clapped. Helen was ever so happy now. At the Final Chorale, the whole school was on the stage, and the children were all waving good-by to the audience, and then there was a silence. Everybody stopped clapping. Helen's voice could be heard singing again, "I am a little Princess, and I'll soon be a Queen."

The audience, and the Teachers again clapped their hands. Helen's mother was as proud as could be. They presented bouquets of flowers to the pianist, and to the Drama Teacher. Then an enormous bouquet of flowers was specially presented to Helen. The Drama Teacher said, in her final speech, that without their deputy actress, Helen, the Princess play could not have been presented.

Helen realised that the Drama Teacher had chosen her specially, because she could absolutely depend upon Helen. Substitutes, Stand-ins, and Deputies were very important people, if they were reliable. Helen was glad she had tried to do her best. The Teacher whispered, "Jesus said that the first shall be last, and the last shall be first." Helen felt sorry for Louise Wilson, so she visited her while she was ill. She was that kind of a girl.

Prayer:

> Lord God, our Father in heaven,
> We thank you for the reliable people,

who step in when things go wrong.
We thank you for substitutes, and deputies.
Teach us that often the first shall be last.
and the last shall become first.   Amen.

Hymn:

Think of all the things we lose. (C&P.1. 57)

Teachers' Note: (1) Explain what it means to "play second fiddle." (2) Substitutes, and stand-ins are specially skilled people, who can play their own part, and other people's parts as well. (3) Jesus said, "He who will be great among you, let him become your servant." Humility is a gift from God.

(b) Helping Hands   *Week 10   Dependable People*

It was Saturday morning in the small country town. It was also market day. The market stalls were lined along the street, and around the old market square. The Traders sold many different kinds of goods. Clothing, towels, second hand ornaments, fruit, flowers, second hand, and new books, leather goods and tools. Patrick and William loved to go walking around the stalls and carts. The Markets Supervisor warned the two boys to get off home. He did not want anyone creating a nuisance in the Market area.

The boys were passing one street-trader, with his handcart full of oranges, which he had parked near the town hall. Something had happened, which caused the Vendor to fall backwards, as he let go of the two handles of his handcart. Now, one should never let down a handcart full of oranges carelessly. The Trader had tripped, and had accidentally fallen. Instead of the handcart falling down on its two legs, it fell backwards, and hundreds of oranges fell off the cart, and rolled all over the road. It was a strange sight to see a narrow street, with oranges rolling about everywhere.

The boys wanted to laugh, but instead, they ran to help the street Trader to his feet again. Patrick and William quickly looked around for an empty cardboard box. They began to pick up the oranges, lying here, there, and everywhere. When the box was filled up, they carefully emptied the oranges back on the handcart. Then, they began all over again. William whispered, "It is a good thing that oranges have strong skins. I don't think that they have suffered much damage."

Patrick looked at the Trader, who had fully recovered from his accidental fall. He looked ever so grateful, that both boys were being so helpful. Soon, six boxes of oranges were poured back, making a small mountain of oranges on the handcart. Another four boxes of oranges were picked up from the street.

"The Trader shouted to the two lads, "Thank you, boys!" You may fill a box of oranges and take them home. It is my way of giving you a reward." The Markets Supervisor was smiling broadly at them. "I was wrong about you two boys. You have been a big help after all." Off they went, carrying the box between them.

William said to Patrick, "What shall we do with a box of oranges? We shall never be able to eat this lot." Patrick, answered, "We could sell them around the doors." "A very good idea, let us try it." Two Police-men saw the two boys, as they drove past in their Panda-car. "Children are not allowed by Law to sell fruit round the doors," they said. Then off the Policemen went.

Patrick said, "If we ate four oranges every day next week at school, we still would have a lot of oranges left." William said, "I think that having to eat four oranges every day, would put me off oranges for life." Patrick thought hard for a moment, then he had a brainwave. "We still have the old Cottage Hospital in Vicarage Lane, let us give them to the sick people at the Hospital."

Off they carried the heavy box of oranges to the little Cottage Hospital. The Chief Nursing Officer received the present graciously. The lady thanked the two boys. She said, "It is always better to give than to receive." The two boys were pleased to have the box of oranges off their hands. They kept away from the Market for quite a long time after that!

Prayer:

> Lord God, our Heavenly Father,
> You give us many good things in life.
> We thank you for food, clothing, and houses.
> We pray for children around the world,
> whose parents help to grow our fruit,
> such as, oranges, melons, grapes, and pine-apples.
> Bless all fruit farmers over-seas.   Amen.

Hymn:

> Pears and apples, wheat and grapes. (C&P.2. 135)

Teachers' Note: (1) Young people love to be helpful. Allow them to list anyone they have helped this week. (2) Accidents are a shock to the people to whom they happen. Accidents are often a time to offer your help. (3) Being a "helper" means that you are sharing someone else's difficult situation.

(c) **Moses the Prince**   *Week 10   Dependable People*

Moses had been brought up as a Prince in the Palace of Egypt. As a baby he had been found in a basket floating among the reeds growing in the river Nile. He really had been born a baby in a Hebrew (Jewish) family of slaves. His parents had hidden him in the basket, because Pharoah, the King, had given out an order that all Hebrew babies were to be killed, in case the Hebrew slave population became larger than the Egyptian people. King Pharoah was afraid that the Hebrews might take over the country from the rule of their masters.

An Egyptian Princess, the daughter of Pharoah, had discovered the baby floating in the basket among the reeds. She took the baby back to live in Pharoah's palace. The Egyptian Princess had named the baby "Moses," which means "Drawn out of the water." She had hired a nurse to take care of the baby. She did not know that the nurse was really Moses' sister. That is how Moses became a royal Prince of Egypt.

In his heart, Moses decided that he was not an Egyptian but a Hebrew. He made up his mind that one day, he would set the Hebrew slaves free. When Moses became a grown up man, he was out one day watching the slaves working, making bricks from the soft clay. After they had laid out the soft clay bricks in the hot Egyptian sunshine, they became hard bricks. Moses saw an Egyptian slave master beating a Hebrew slave with his whip. Moses became so angry with the slave master, that he fought him and killed the slave master. He hid his body in the sand.

Another day, Moses saw two Hebrew slaves fighting with each other. He tried to stop the two slaves fighting. One of the slaves said to Moses. "Stop your interfering with us. Do you think that you will kill us, just as you killed that Egyptian." Moses realised that what had happened, was known among the people, and he was afraid that the account might reach the ears of Pharoah. Then he himself would be killed. So he ran away to a desert country.

God knew that Moses had made a mistake in killing the Egyptian slave master. God really had chosen Moses to be the leader of the slaves, and to lead them out of Egypt, into freedom. Moses was alone in the desert feeling very sorry for himself when he saw a strange sight. A bush was burning, yet it was not reduced to ashes. He approached the bush. The voice of God said, from the burning bush, "Moses take off your shoes, because you are standing on holy ground. (A sign of respect among Hebrews).

God spoke from out of the bush again. "Moses I have heard the cries of my people, the Hebrews, as they are being beaten by their task masters. I have chosen you to become their Leader. I want to to go to Pharoah, and tell him that you are going to lead the people out of Egypt." Moses was more afraid than ever. He said to God, "I cannot go to Pharoah, I am a slow speaker." God answered, "I will send Aaron, your brother, to be your Assistant." This is how Moses became Leader of the Hebrew people. Later he helped them to escape. He led the Hebrews through the Red Sea to freedom. A strong wind blew back the tide, and all the slave people escaped over the sand on dry land, to begin their march to the Promised land. (known as Israel today).

Prayer:

> Father God, we pray that wrong-doing
> may cease among all people.
> We pray that we may grow to love each other,
> as Jesus taught us.
> Forgive us if we have sinned against
> someone else.
> In your mercy protect us all.   Amen.

Hymn:

Spirit of peace, come to our waiting world. (C&P.2. 85)

Teachers' Note: (1) God provided for the escape of the Hebrew slaves, by allowing Moses to be born in the palace of Pharoah. (2) Moses was too quick tempered when he killed the Egyptian task master. That was wrong. (3) Some things that seem impossible, in God's good time, work out for good. The Hebrews became the Jewish race of people, who inhabited the land of Israel and spread around the world. Reference Exodus Chapters 2-4.

(a) Albert Schweitzer

Week 11   Hospitals

In the year 1875, a little baby born in the country of Alsace, which is an area on the borders of France and Germany. The baby was just like any other baby, and at the time, no-one realised that this infant was to grow up to be a very clever person, indeed. They called the little baby Albert. His surname was "Schweitzer." At school, in the Munster Valley, he was always at the top of the class. Learning anything came very easily to him. Little Albert loved to learn.

As a child he loved music. When he became a man, he studied the Organ, eventually he went to Paris, where he became a Doctor of Music. Albert made a vow that he would study science and art until he was thirty years old. After that he would give his life to helping other people.

Next, Albert studied religious subjects. He became a Doctor of Philosophy. Then he became a Curate of St. Nicholas Church, in Strasburg. After that, he became a teacher at the the University. In time, he became the Principal of his College. He also wrote a book about the musical composer, J. S. Bach. Soon he wrote yet another book about preserving old organs. Albert was a very practical scholar.

As if he had not enough of learning, Albert now began to study to be Doctor of Medicine. Of course, he had to resign as Principal of his College, to find the time to study medicine. He married. It took him seven years study, to become a Medical Doctor. Now, he was a Doctor of Music, a Doctor of Philosophy, and a Doctor of Medicine? He could easily have become a rich man, settled down in a large house, and became famous.

Instead, Dr. Albert Schweitzer and his wife, travelled to what was known then, as French Equatorial Africa. He set up a hospital at Lambarene. In that area, thousands of people were suffering from either Leprosy, a dreaded skin disease, or from sleeping-sickness. People died every day from these illnesses. There were very few people with skills enough to help them.

Albert's hospital was not like any hospital you have ever seen. It was more like a make-shift hospital. People lay on blankets on the ground, inside straw and mud huts. He knew that people needed help immediately. Albert's knowledge and medicines began to help and cure the poor sick people.

He began to train nurses and medical helpers. When he ran short of money for his hospital medicines, Albert would come back to Europe, and he would book halls in the large cities. Many people would come to hear Albert Schweitzer playing the famous city organs of the time. The money people paid for their seats, Albert used to pay for the cost of more medicines, which he needed for his African hospital in Lambarene. Then, he would go back to his hospital, to carry on with his work of healing.

Albert had one important belief. He named it himself as, "reverence for life". Everything he ever did to help the poor people of West Africa, was because he believed that African people were all members of God's family. Albert died aged ninety, in 1965, after a life-time of helping Africans. Many Lepers, and people who had suffered from sleeping sickness thanked God, for the medical knowledge, and loving care of Albert Schweitzer.

Albert was like a working horse. He was happy while working, and learning. The reason why children need to work hard at school is that they will want to be successful and helpful to others, when they grow older. There is an old saying which says that knowledge is power.

Prayer:

>   Father God, whose family is made up
>   of all people everywhere,
>   we thank you for the life of Albert Schweitzer.
>   Bless all Doctors and Nurses,
>   who help in the great work of healing.
>   Bless all sick children everywhere.   Amen.

124

Hymn:

Make me a channel of your peace. (C&P.2. 147)

Teachers Note: (1) Albert Schweitzer was a Doctor of Music, Religion, and of Medicine. Yet he was once a little boy, who tried hard to learn at school. (2) Hospitals first came into being by the efforts of the Christian Church (3) People overseas need the same standard of medical care as we do. Jesus on occasions healed lepers. The good new is that Leprosy may be cured today, by medical injections.

(b) Good Friends   *Week 11   Hospitals*

Charlie and Christopher were best friends, when they attended school in their village. They knew the names of all the birds in the woods. The used to fish together beside the wheel on the mill pond. They helped farmer Nugent during the harvest season. They sat together in the back seat of the Methodist chapel on a Sunday morning. They lived during the years before the First World War. There were not many motor cars on the roads. They remembered seeing the first motor-cycle accident. This was before the present 'Halt' signs were erected on the 'T' junctions in their village.

When the 1914 war was declared, both boys were just eighteen. They joined the same regiment in the army. They were volunteers in those days, as conscription into the Forces came years later. Both lads were sent to France, to fight in the terrible trench warfare. The shells coming across the sky, were blowing up the trees and hedges, and Charlie and Chris were sorry to see all the destruction. The war dragged on for four years, and soldiers were killed in thousands in their section of the front line.

The soldiers lived and slept in the trenches, which were dug into the French soil. Lines of barbed wire were everywhere. Many young soldiers were wounded, maimed, blinded, or killed every day. War is such a waste of good people's lives. The Red Cross had little field hospitals behind the lines. Wounded soldiers were taken by stretcher to the field hospitals. They were given first aid, and then carried by army truck to the seaport. From there, they were transported back to England to a real hospital.

One day, the command was given that the Regiment was to attack the enemy lines only a few hundred metres away. The ground in between the two armies was known as "No man's land." Any soldiers seen on this land would be shot by the enemy. The Regiment had to advance across no-mans land on this occasion.

Along with hundreds of others, Charlie and Chris advanced with their rifles at the ready, but in the smoke and noise, they became separated. Charlie was hit by a bullet in the leg, and he fell into a shell hole. When the Regiment came back to their trenches again, they usually counted their dead men, and the number who were wounded. Charlie could not be found, so he was listed as "missing."

Chris waited all day, until it became dark that evening. He knew that Charlie was lying somewhere in no-mans-land. Perhaps he was dead, but maybe he might still be alive. Chris asked permission from his Commanding Officer to go out at night to search for Charlie. He was given permission. So when the stretcher bearers were carrying back the dead soldiers, Chris set out to look for his friend, Charlie. It was a pitch black night. Chris crawled over the wet mud. He prayed that the moon might not shine that night, and reveal him to the enemy lines.

He had crawled for what seemed to be a long way in the dark, when he had an idea. He whistled like the skylark, three times, just as they did when they were boys. Charlie was lying in great pain in a wet shell hole in the ground. Suddenly, in the darkness, he heard a skylark whistling. He knew that skylarks did not whistle at night. He remembered that his best friend, Chris, used to make that sound at school.

Even though Charlie was in terrible pain, he managed to make three whistle sounds in the darkness. Chris heard him, and now he knew that his friend Charlie was alive. Chris slowly crawled towards the place where he had heard the sound. Eventually, he found Charlie lying in the muddy hole. The first thing Charlie said, was, "It is you Chris! I always knew that you would come!"

Christopher put Charlie over his shoulder, and carried him back in the darkness to the Field hospital. He stumbled often, but eventually both men were safe behind the British Lines. Soon, Charlie was transported back to a hospital in England. After months in hospital, he recovered and was able to walk again.

After six months the War was over. Chris came home with his regiment, and Charlie was waiting for him at the ship's gangway. The two comrades were glad to settle down again in their lovely little village. Both married village girls, and lived happy ever after. When they became old men, they used to sit on the bench on the village green, and talk about the past happy and sad times. They always stopped talking, and little tears would come into their eyes, when they heard the skylark singing in the sky. Can you guess why?

The important part of this story is what Charlie said, lying in the shell-hole, in the darkness, "It is you Chris? I always knew that you would come." He believed that his best friend would risk his own life, to come and rescue him. The Bible tells us that there is a friendship that is closer than a brother's. Jesus once said, "You are my friends." Jesus was willing to die for his friends. Christians believe that Jesus will come into the lives of all who pray and ask him.

Prayer:

    Good Lord, we thank you for the love,
    shown in the example of Jesus who gave his life for us.

Today, we thank you for the friendship of God's people.
Teach us to respect one another.   Amen.

Hymn:

I danced in the morning. (C&P.1. 22) (JP. 91)

Teachers' Note: (1) It is good to have real friends. (2) Charlie and Christopher were friends all their lives. (3) Chris was willing to risk his own life to save Charlie.

(c) The Good Samaritan   *Week 11   Hospitals*

There was once a merchant, who was travelling from Jerusalem, down the road to Jericho. He was riding a donkey, which had two panniers strapped on each side of the donkey, to carry his merchandise. He had a good days' trading. He had sold a lot of cloth in the Jerusalem market. The money he had received, he had put inside a leather purse. The purse he had hidden inside his jerkin.

It was a very hot day, and the road to Jericho went down into the valley. This made the journey even hotter, because in the valley, there was not much wind to cool him down. It was not a road, as we understand roads. It was more of a small track for horse riders.

As the merchant reached the lower stretch of the journey, a gang of bandits were lying in wait behind the large rocks. The bandits jumped out, and knocked the merchant off his donkey. They attacked him, and beat him, just as some people are mugged nowadays. They took everything valuable which he was carrying. Inside his jacket, they found his purse of money, which he was taking home. Having robbed him, they left him for dead.

The poor man was lying bruised and bleeding under the hot sun. A Levite from the old family of Levi, who sang in the Temple choir, came passing the same way. He did not stop to offer any help. Instead, the Levite passed by on the other side of the path, pretending he had not seen the poor bleeding victim. Later, a Priest, came down the road, and he too passed by on the other side, because he was afraid that the bandits might still be hanging about. The priest knew that he ought to have offered help, but he did nothing.

Now a Samaritan came riding a donkey down the path. He was from a country quite close, whom the Jewish people in those days would despise, because Samaritans were thought to follow a less true religion. In those days, the Jews looked down on Samaritans, because they did not worship at the Temple in Jerusalem. St. John's Gospel says that the Jews had no dealings with the Samaritans. So this Samaritan had every reason to pass by. Yet when he saw the poor traveller, lying in the hot sunshine, bruised and bleeding badly, the Samaritan stopped his donkey.

He went over to the wounded merchant, and helped him. He bathed his bruises, and poured in oil, and wine to clean up the wounds. He lifted the wounded merchant on to his donkey, and carried him carefully along the road to the nearest hotel. The Samaritan paid for the stay of the wounded traveller. He also assured the hotel-keeper, that if keeping the wounded traveller until he was better, cost any more, that he would pay the extra costs, the next time he was passing. The Hotel-keeper and the Samaritan traveller shook hands and parted. The wounded man gradually became well again.

Jesus told this story because a lawyer had asked Jesus, the question, "Who is my neighbour?" Instead of answering the lawyer immediately, Jesus told this story. He expected the lawyer to understand from the story, that anyone who needs our care and help, is our neighbour, even though he might be from another race, or country.

Nowadays, the ambulance is the good Samaritan in our towns. When someone is knocked down on the road by a motor car, and is badly hurt, the 999 telephone call will bring the Para-Medics in the ambulance to help. When we pay our taxes, we are paying for the care and upkeep of people who are sick in hospital. All hospital-care costs money.

Prayer:
> Lord, our heavenly Father, we thank you,
> for the story of the good Samaritan.
> On the road of life, inspire us to help others,
> who may have been hurt in some way.
> Teach us what human compassion means.
> May we try to be friendly to others.   Amen.

Hymn:
> I was lying in the roadway. (C&P.2. 88), or
> When I needed a neighbour were you there? (C&P.1. 65) (JP. 275)

Teacher's Note: (1) This story may be known to the children, but it is worth while repeating, because it is relevant. (today's street mugging criminals. Ask them to quote a parallel happening from the T.V. or newspapers. (2) The traveller may have been foolish to travel alone in such a dangerous lonely place, but it was common practice. (3) The Samaritan freely gave help, even though the other religions might not have liked him.

(a) The Towel

(The Teacher will need three objects for the following three Assemblies this week. (1). A brightly coloured clean towel. (2.) Two pieces of wood, one longer than the other, to make a "cross." (3). A chocolate, or a real egg).

Jesus and his twelve friends (disciples) had been on a journey, and the roads had been very dusty. The sun had been shining fiercely all day, so by the time they arrived at the house, where they were going to stay, their feet and sandals were very dusty. There were no tarmacadam roads in those days. Usually a servant would meet the guests as soon as they arrived. The servant would offer to wash the feet of the visitors. On this occasion, no servant was there to attend the guests.

Inside the house, the twelve men looked at each other. Each of the disciples wondered who was going to become a servant to the others. Who was going to wash the visitors' dirty, sweaty feet? Each man, Peter, James, John, Phillip, Judas, to name but a few, were all too proud to act as servants.

To the surprise of the twelve men, Jesus their leader, brought a basin, and poured water into it. He took a towel on his arm. Jesus, then knelt down, and he went round the circle of men in the room, washing, and then, drying each man's feet, with great care. By his action, Jesus showed his friends that they must not be proud. They must be humble enough to serve each other.

When Jesus came to Simon Peter, Peter felt so ashamed that Jesus, their Lord, was taking a servant's position in the group, that he said, "Lord, I will not allow you to wash my feet." Jesus answered, "Peter, you do not realise what I am doing now, but later you will understand. If I do not wash your feet, then we cannot be friends."

Peter, then went to the other extreme. He said, Lord, "Do not just wash my feet, but wash my hands and my head as well." Jesus replied, "If a person already had had a bath, then they only need to wash their feet. You call me Teacher, and Lord. and this you do correctly, because that is what I am. Now if I, your Lord, and Teacher, have washed your feet, you also should wash one another's feet. No servant is greater than his Master. Now that you know these facts, you will be blessed, if you do them."

Have you ever watched a football team come out of the dressing rooms on a wet day. The field may be squelchy with mud. After kicking the ball up and down the field, both teams' strips may have become filthy. Imagine that you have a super-goal-keeper, and he manages to keep the ball out of his goals, through-out the match. Imagine that your team scores five lovely goals.

Imagine that the team's football strip, worn by every player, after the game, is now dirty with the muddy state of the pitch. The players troop off to have a hot bath. They throw away their dirty football strips, and put on their normal clothes again. Who is going to wash the teams' dirty clothing?

The goalie is important, but the person who washes and irons the football strip, for next week's game is also very important too! What if your team had to play in dirty strips next Saturday? The players would be ashamed, and their supporters would also be ashamed of them. So the person who washes and irons, and sorts out the strips, is very important to the success of the team. Don't you? Important people are those who are willing to serve others!

Prayer:

Lord of Easter, we thank you for the humility
of the Lord Jesus Christ.
Make us willing to be humble enough
that also we may be willing to serve other people.
We pray for important people who do dirty jobs in life.
Help us to value them for their good work.   Amen.

Hymn:

Jesus in the garden. (C&P.2. 129)

Teachers' Note: (1) The servant's towel in the story shows humility for those who use it. (2) The towel also carries the meaning of cleanliness. (3) The meaning is that we must be willing to be helpful to human need. We all depend on the good work of other people, in order to live. Reference St. Luke 22, verse 27, and John Chapter 13, verses 3-9.

(b) The Cross
Week 12   Towards Easter

(The Teacher will need two pieces of wood, one shorter than the other, for this Assembly).

Where do these two pieces of wood come into the Easter story. They may be used to make the letter "T", (demonstrate), but that is not the answer. They could be used to make the letter "L" (demonstrate). Again, this is not the answer.

Watch carefully, as I stretch out my arms just this once. Now do you know what two pieces of wood were once used for? Yes! They were used to make a cross. Did you know that there are three crosses on the "Union Jack," the national flag of Great Britain?

St. Patrick's cross is the diagonal white cross on a red background.

St. Georges' cross is the perpendicular and horizontal white cross on a red background.

St. Andrews' cross is the diagonal white cross on a blue background.

Did you know that when the Roman Court condemned law-breakers to death, that the condemned men had to carry the cross-beam of their cross on their shoulders. The whole cross would often be too heavy for the condemned person to carry through the streets, to the place of execution. Jesus was our Lord, and also he was a good man, who was killed on a cross by Roman soldiers.

Have you ever been to the Lake District. There are many lovely lakes, which you could walk around. Some are too large to get round in one walk. However, there is at least, one beautiful Lake, which your Mum and Dad could easily take you around for an enjoyable walk. It is called Lake Buttermere. When you get the opportunity to go to Lake Buttermere, after you walk half way around the water, look up at the mountainside, just behind the farm. There you will see a cross on the hillside, quite high up.

A young climber was climbing up the rocky hillside, when he accidentally slipped and fell down. Sad to relate, he was killed. His friends marked the place on the mountain where he fell, by erecting a cross. It remains to this day, as a monument to the brave young climber who fell to his death. It is strange, but we often remember brave people who die, by using the sign of the cross.

During the wars, very brave people were given the Victoria Cross, or the George Cross, for bravery and sacrifice. The reason we remember people in this way, is because Jesus was nailed to two pieces of wood. He died hanging between two thieves, who also were dying on crosses for doing wrong. Jesus in contrast to the two thieves had done no wrong. It was a cruel and lingering way to die. He was made to die the death of a criminal. Many things which Jesus touched, were changed for the good. So it comes about, that the cross, which was meant to frighten bad people, became the sign of bravery for good people, because the bravest man who ever lived, Jesus of Nazareth, died in this manner.

One of the great artists painted a picture of Jesus as a young boy, working in his father's workshop. The sun is shining through the window. It is evening, and the sun is casting shadows. The young boy, Jesus, is tired, and he is shown stretching his arms out sideways. At that very moment the sun shines brightly, and causes the shadow of a cross to appear on the wall, behind where the boy is standing. It is as if the shadow of the cross was hanging over Jesus, even from the days when he was a boy. This is the lesson the artist meant us to understand, by his painting.

Prayer:

> Father, we thank you that Jesus
> always changed things for the better.
> We rejoice that the sad day of crucifixion,
> became known as, "Good Friday."
> We pray for anyone who bears a cross
> of sickness, or handicap in this life.

Bless them specially, and give them hope,
at Easter time,   Amen.

Hymn:

There is a green hill far away. (JP. 245)

Teachers' Note: (1) The cross is the sign of the Christian Church. (2) The cross is the sign of bravery. (3) Many people have to bear the cross of illness, or pain, or handicap in their private lives. Let us also be brave for God!

(c) The Egg

(A large chocolate Easter egg, or a real egg would suitably illustrate this story.)

Emma was a farmer's daughter. She was ten years old. One day on the farm, she was walking around the hay-shed, when she happened to see a huge egg in the hay. Emma had never seen an egg so big as that before. She brought it to her Dad, the farmer.

He laughed and said, "Emma, this is a goose's egg. The goose must have just laid it, it was not there five minutes ago. Feel it! It is quite warm. Let us put the egg in the Goose shed. There is one old goose which will sit on it, until it hatches." They put the large egg into a box of straw, and sure enough, the old goose sat on top of the egg, and kept it warm.

Dad and Emma took a look at the egg every day. In nearly four weeks time, the big egg began to crack open. Out waddled a tiny gosling. The little gosling followed the old goose everywhere. Emma was delighted with the beautiful little gosling.

Now children, can you think why an egg reminds us of Easter? Jesus was not buried in a grave in a church-yard. No! His body was put into a hole in the rock, similar to a cave. The grave was known as a tomb. A large stone was placed at the entrance to the tomb. When Jesus arose from the dead, the disciples found that the stone had been rolled away. They found that Jesus had gone. Now, an egg is like a tomb. The little gosling eventually breaks out of the egg, and walks away. So eggs remind us of the Easter story.

Jesus arose from the dead, and went elsewhere. When Mary Magdalene went to visit the tomb, very early on the first Easter morning, it was still dark, because the sun had not yet risen. Mary Magdalene saw that the stone had been rolled away from the tomb, and that the tomb was empty. She ran as fast as she could to tell Peter and John. She breathlessly told them, "They have rolled the stone away, and they have taken the Lord out of the tomb. I do not know where they have laid him".

Peter and John ran as fast as they could to the garden. John ran faster than Peter, and so he arrived first. John looked inside the tomb, but he did not enter it. He saw the strips of linen cloth neatly folded inside. Then, Peter arrived running, gasping for breath. Peter was more daring than John, so he entered the tomb. He too saw the linen cloths lying folded, and the cloth napkin, which had been covering the face of Jesus, was also folded, but lying apart. It was the custom in those days for dead people to be bandaged up, before they were buried in the grave. Peter and John having looked into the tomb, went home again.

By that time Mary Magdalene had returned to the garden tomb. The morning sunlight was becoming brighter. Mary was crying quietly to herself. She looked inside the tomb, and she saw two angel messengers dressed in white, sitting, one at the head, and one at the foot of the place where Jesus had been lying. The angel messengers asked her, why she was crying? She replied, "They have taken my Lord away, and I do not know where they have laid him."

Mary turned away, from the tomb, and Jesus himself was standing behind her. Mary did not know it was Jesus. She thought that the man behind her was the gardener. The stranger said to her, "Woman, why are you weeping. Who is it that you are looking for? Mary Magdalene, even yet, thought it was the gardener. She answered, "Sir, if you have carried him away, tell me where you have put him."

Jesus quietly said to her, "Mary," and instantly, Mary Magdalene knew that voice so well. She knew it was Jesus, and that he was alive. He had risen from the dead. Mary could only say "Master." (Meaning "Teacher"). She was so excited and full of joy. Jesus said to her, "Go and tell my brothers the good news." Mary went back to the disciples who were living in Jerusalem, full of joy and hope, to tell them that she had seen a living Jesus.

Prayer:

> Blessed Father of our Lord Jesus,
> we thank you for that first Easter morning.
> We are so happy that Jesus arose from the tomb.
> We are glad that Mary was the first person
> to bring the good news that Jesus was alive.
> Help us to understand the meaning of Easter Day.   Amen.

Hymn:

> All in an Easter garden. (C&P.2. 130)
> or, I serve a risen saviour. (JP. 113)

Teachers' Note: (1) The egg illustrates the opening of the tomb. (2) The disciples did not expect the Resurrection, so it came as a complete surprise. (3) Mary went to visit the tomb, like any woman might go to visit the grave of a deceased loved one. She was the first Evangelist of the Resurrection. Reference. St. John Gospel, Chapter 20 verses 1-18.

Summer Term

(a) April Fool

Katie and her best friend, Stephanie, were very happy because April the first had arrived on the calender. At school they both put their heads together, and made up secret plans to have some fun, at someone else's expense. The day was known as "April Fool's day. They decided to wait until Jan went out of the class-room at play-time, then they would take her lunch box out of her school bag, and hide it.

They pretended to be good friends with Jan that morning. When she left the room, they opened her bag, and took her lunch box. They hid it in the "Lost Property" box along the corridor. They giggled and winked among themselves when Jan came back into the room. Jan felt terribly alone, when the others were laughing at her, because children like to be good friends with everyone. Jan did not know what the joke was about.

At dinner time, Jan opened her bag to discover that her lunch box was missing. She felt sure that her Mum had put it into her school bag that morning. However, she could not be sure. She used the telephone to contact her Mum at home. Mum told Jan over the telephone, that the lunch box had been in her school bag, when she went out to school that morning. Jan now knew that someone had deliberately removed her lunch.

She searched the class-room, and then looked into the "Lost Property" box in the corridor. She saw her lunch box lying along with lost shoes, tee-shirts, and smelly socks, and other lost goods. Jan felt that she could not eat food from such an un-hygienic place, so she threw the pieces of bread up into the air to feed the sea-gulls flying overhead. She never said a word to anyone at lunch time. She simply took a drink of water, instead.

Meanwhile, Katie and Stephanie had forgotten about Jan. Both girls where playing on top of the old boilerhouse wall. Then, the girls climbed on the slates of the boilerhouse. Katie slipped and grabbed hold of Stephanie and both girls fell on to the ground below. They were screaming loudly. Jan was the first to hear them. She ran with the others to help the two girls up on their feet again.

Katie had hurt her arm badly, and cut her knees. Stephanie had scraped the side of her leg all the way down to the ankle. She had also twisted her foot in the fall. It was as if someone was repaying the two unkind girls with some punishment. Although the truth was that they had brought the punishment upon themselves.

Jan ran for the Head Teacher, who took the girls into her room, for First Aid treatment. The Doctor was called, since he lived nearby. The Head Teacher telephoned their parents, and asked them to take Katie and Stephanie home. Afterwards, Jan and her Mum talked it over together, about what they should do. They both guessed who had hidden Jan's lunch box in the Lost Property box.

Jan's Mum gave her money to send flowers to both Katie's and Stephanie's home by telephone. This means that a local florist's shop received the order, and that later he delivered the flowers by van. The girls read their cards, "Love from Jan, get well soon!" Both girls felt ashamed of themselves.

Question: Do you think that Jan acted in a wise manner, or not? When they returned to school, weeks afterwards, Jan welcomed them back, with a smile. Katie and Stephanie never played April Fool on anyone else, because they knew that their prank had been a very cruel one. Maybe, it was not Jan who was the April Fool, but Katie and Stephanie themselves, who really had been the two April fools! Jan, on the other hand, used to say to herself, "Forgiveness is sweet."

Prayer:

> Gracious Lord God, whose name is "Love",
> Teach us to be forgiving and kind,
> even to those who would do us harm.
> May we understand what it means
> to forgive seventy times seven.   Amen

Hymn:

> Join with us to sing God's praises. (C&P.1. 30)
> or, Jubilate, everybody. (JP. 145)

Teachers' Note: (1) April Fool's Day is not a day to hurt other people. (2) Sometimes life has punishments for cruel people. (3) Jan believed that forgiveness is always sweet. Although it is not always easy to forgive.

(b) A Wise Fool
Week 1   Fools

There once was a man who had a strange job in life. He was known as a "fool", because he was the Jester or entertainer in the king's court. His profession was to play the fool, and try to keep everyone happy. We have a lot of Jesters on television nowadays. Can you name any?

Long ago, a king always had many Advisors around him, when people were asking questions about land, or taxes, or law problems. He also needed these important people to help him make decisions about the kingdom. Sometimes the King became tired, because he had to make so many difficult decisions. The court Jester, would come along when the king was feeling gloomy, or sad. The Jester would crack jokes, or perform tricks, or juggle plates on the top of bamboo canes to cheer up the King.

There was a small Chapel in the King's Palace. Last thing each evening, the Jester used to go down to the palace chapel to pray to God. After he said his prayers, the Jester used to do a little dance before the chapel altar table. It was reported to the King that the Jester was dancing alone in the Chapel every night.

The King called for his Jester to stand before him. He said, "What is this. I hear about your dancing in the Chapel every night. Surely, that is not a respectful thing to do in Church?"

The Jester answered the King. "What I do as a Jester is my only talent. I offer entertainment and happiness to anyone who will listen to me. I even offer my jokes and wisecracks to you, your majesty. You accept my skills, and you laugh at my jokes. When I myself feel downhearted, I juggle and dance before the chapel altar table. I offer the best that I can do, to the Lord God himself. I can imagine the good Lord smiling at my efforts. Is that not a wise thing to do, your Majesty?"

The good King smiled at his Jester. He said, "I am sure that you are right. We can all offer our best work to God. This is your work. Why should you not offer your juggling and dances to God? If you do that, then you will never perform or say anything that is bad."

After that, each night the Jester continued to perform his dances before the Lord, alone in the Chapel. No one, except the King, ever knew that he could not read the Bible, nor the hymn-book, nor the prayer book. No one ever knew that the Jester had never gone to school. This was the Jester's own way of praying, and praising God.

Do you think that the Jester was right? Children can offer what they learn each day at school to God when they say their prayers. If you do this, then you will always try to do your best in your school work. There is a verse in th Bible which says, "Shall I offer to God that which cost me nothing?" This means we must put our hearts into anything we do, if we want to offer it unto God.

Prayer:

> Heavenly Father, Lord of all of life,
> Help us to prepare ourselves for
> the journey of living in God's world.
> As we learn from our teachers,
> and as we learn from each other,
> may we follow Jesus as our guide.   Amen.

Hymn:

> One more step along the world I go. (C&P.1. 47), (JP. 188)

Teachers' Note: (1) The king was solving other people's problems. Children also sometimes have little worries. (2) The Jester was one of those wise people who could tell the truth, and yet make people laugh. (3) School is a preparation place for living. We offer our best work to God. The more we put into school, the more we get out of education.

(c) People who are like Animals   *Week 1   Fools*

Jesus knew that King Herod was a bad king. One day he said, "Go and tell that fox Herod." He was using the name of an animal to explain to the people just what kind of a person King Herod really was. If a fox gets into a hen-house at night, it will not just steal one hen. Rather, it will kill all the hens in the hen-house. A fox can be very cunning and cruel. Jesus thought of King Herod as being a cruel bad king, so he called him a "fox".

Sometimes when we see people out walking their dog, we look at them, and we think that the dog is a little like the person who is taking it for a walk. Sometimes a country uses an animal to explain the character of the people. The British Nation is sometimes referred to as John Bull. (John Bull was a sturdy man with a top hat, a Union Jack for his shirt, and he always was accompanied by his Bull-dog). This bull-dog is supposed to be like the British People's character. The Bull-dog is not afraid of the Bull. The Nation would like to think that we all are dependable like the Bull-dog.

People can be a little like animals. Jesus once called the Jewish Leaders "serpents". What do you think he meant? Isaiah says that we are all like sheep who have gone astray. When Jesus once told a story about ninety-nine sheep, and one lost sheep. He was referring to people.

Now we are going to try to to think of people who act like animals.

As sly as a …?	(fox)	He was as slow as …?	(a snail or tortoise)
As strong as an …?	(ox)	She was as wise as …?	(an owl)
He ran like a …?	(hare)	He was as stubborn as …?	(a mule)
He roars like a …?	(bull)	She eats like a …?	(horse)
He is as greedy as a …?	(pig)	She was as quiet as a …?	(mouse)
He was as brave as a …?	(lion)	He could swim like a …?	(fish)
He could see like a …?	(hawk)	She could sleep like a …?	(dormouse)
He was as busy as a …?	(bee)	She worked like an …?	(ant)
He could jump like a …?	(kangaroo)	She could sing like a …?	(nightingale)
He was like a …… in a china shop.	(bull)		
She grins like a …… ……	(Cheshire Cat)		

An Ostrich is a large bird, which can run quickly, because it has long legs. It is taller than a man. Yet the ostrich is a very foolish bird. When the hunters chase the ostrich, the bird will run until it becomes tired. Then it will put its head into a bush, thinking that because he cannot see what is happening, the hunters cannot see him. Oliver was a large ostrich, who pecked about the desert all day. He could run very fast.

One day, the Arab hunters came on their beautiful horses to catch him. Oliver ran with great long strides, leaving the horses behind. Then when he became tired, he buried his head in the sand, and because he could not see anyone, he thought he was hidden. Of course, the Arab hunters killed him, and ate him up for their dinner. Poor Oliver was a rather foolish bird.

There was another Oliver, who was a bright little boy. He used to steal chocolates and sweets from the shops, and because he thought that no-one saw him, he believed that he would never be caught. Unknown to Oliver, most of the shops, kept several video-cameras hidden above the doorways, and behind the chocolate shelves. It was not until a white and orange police car drew up outside his house, that Oliver became very much afraid. The police lady and the policeman showed video's of Oliver stealing from the shops. Oliver had been a foolish boy, as well as a bad boy. The Police told his Dad and Mum, and his Head Teacher what he had been doing. Oliver realised that people had been watching him for a long time. He felt that he had been a little like the silly Ostrich. He never stole from shops ever again. Think about this question. What sort of an animal are you like?

Prayer:

> Hear us, Father God of all that is good.
> You have set us in a world of time.
> May we not waste our precious moments.
> Teach us to always be wise and honest,
> that people may be able to trust us at all times.
> to God's glory, and to help ourselves,
> and other people.   Amen.

Hymn:

> Thank you Lord, for this new day. (C&P.1. 32), (JP. 232)

Teachers' Notes: (1) It is true that people may be a little like animals. 2. Because we are human beings, and must be honest at all times, we must live better than animals. The Ten Commandments say, "Thou shalt not steal. 3. Oliver became a thief. Even if the television cannot film us, we should remember that God always sees what we do. We must not bring disgrace upon our family or school by stealing. God can forgive us, and we may make a new start.

(a) David is Anointed King

Saul was the first king which the Hebrew people ever had. At the beginning, he had ruled the kingdom fairly well. However, he seems to have had a sickness of the mind, which made him a very moody person at times. He would become depressed, and jealous. Sometimes he would throw his javelin at the musician, who was playing the harp, and trying to cheer him up.

God spoke to Samuel the prophet, (God's special Hebrew preacher) and told him that Saul had been rejected as king. When Saul heard that God was going to put another person as king on his throne, he became very anxious. He clutched the Prophet Samuel's coat roughly, and he tore it. Samuel turned to face king Saul, and he said, "This is how your kingdom will be torn out of your hands."

The Lord sent Samuel to go and search for the next person to be King of Israel. (of the Hebrew people). Samuel was told to to anoint (to pour a horn of oil over the head of) the future chosen man to be King. Off the Prophet Samuel went. God instructed Samuel that he was to visit Bethlehem. "Go to the home of Jesse the farmer. One of his sons may be the person I have chosen to become the next King of Israel."

Samuel, met Jesse. When his sons came to share in the worship of the Lord, Samuel looked at these fine young men. However, none of them seemed to be the right person to be the next king. God said to Samuel, "People generally choose by what they can see from the outside of a person. I am the Lord, and I choose people by what I can see in their hearts. I am looking for good character."

Samuel asked Jesse the farmer, "Are these all your sons?" Jesse answered, "There is yet one son, but he is the youngest. He is out in the fields caring for my sheep." Samuel said, "Jessie, bring him in to me." David, the youngest son, was brought into the house. He was a strong and a very handsome young man, with a bright look in his eyes, and sun-burnt cheeks.

God spoke to Samuel, not aloud for others to hear, but rather he spoke to the Prophet Samuel quietly in his mind. God wanted to appoint the best person at that time, for the difficult position as King. Samuel was assured in his mind that David was the right man to be anointed as King.

"This is the man whom I have chosen to be the future King of my people, Israel" At that moment, God sent his Spirit into David's heart. The Prophet, Samuel, took a horn of oil from under his coat. David knelt before the Prophet. Samuel poured the oil over David's head, anointing him as the future king of Israel. Then, Samuel left Jesse's sheep-farm, and went on his way. David went back to tending his sheep.

It is always difficult to chose people to be Leaders of other people. When you go up to the secondary school, you will find that in the Fifth or Sixth Form, the school will choose people to become Prefects. These are either older girls or boys, who will receive a special place over the other pupils, because they can be trusted to act fairly at all times. A school Prefect, like any Leader, must remember to keep the rules of the school, and to be a genuine help to younger pupils. They must have good characters.

Prayer:

> Heavenly Father, our gracious God,
> We thank you for the story
> of the anointing of King David.
> Help us to strive after that good character,
> that will enable us to be trusted in school   Amen.

Hymn:

> What about being old Moses. (C&P.2. 81)

Teachers' Note: (1) King Saul was like some good people, who sometimes backslide from their former good character. (2) It is always difficult to choose people to serve others. A National Election is our method today of choosing our Leaders. (3) The important fact was that God poured his Spirit upon David. This is the secret which gave David his inner strength. Reference 1 Samuel 16.

(b) The May Queen
Week 2   Leadership

The small Church had a May Queen every year. The custom was to appoint four other girls to be Ladies-in Waiting to the May Queen. However, there was a problem! The girl who had been chosen to be Queen the year before, had emigrated to Australia with her parents. She would not be coming back. The Committee of the Church had to decide, whom they would appoint, in the place of the absent girl.

There was the rule, held for many years at the Church, that the May Queen had to be chosen from the girls aged eleven, who had attended the Sunday school, every Sunday over the past year. Most girls of eleven years were beginning to neglect attending Sunday school, so that made the choice very difficult, indeed.

One Sunday, the special speaker at the Church, was a Lady Missionary Nurse, who had just returned to England, from Swaziland. She had been granted a furlough (holiday) with six months leave of absence. To everyone's delight, the Missionary Nurse had brought a Swazi girl home with her. The Girl had been baptised into the Christian Church, in South Africa, and was named "Rachel." Both Rachel's parents had died, when she was very young. The Missionary Nurse had brought up the orphan girl, as her own daughter. Rachel looked up to the Nurse as her mother and her protector.

The children at the Church Sunday school were amazed that Rachel could speak English so fluently. Rachel explained that she had attended the Mission boarding school, where she had been taught English, and also her own Swazi language. She explained that she was eleven years of age, and that she hoped she would be able to stay at boarding school in South Africa, until she was at least sixteen years old. She hoped that one day, she also could train to be a nurse, and serve her own Swazi people.

The listening children were fascinated by Rachel. She was very tall for her age. She wore a brightly coloured dress, and white sandals. She repeated poetry in the Swazi Language, and then in English. She could sing beautifully. She showed the children a long snake-skin, a Zulu shield, and animal heads carved from wood.

Rachel explained that she was a daughter of a Swazi Paramount Chief. At that moment, the Sunday School Superintendent realised that, maybe, this was God's answer to her prayer. So she asked Rachel, whether she ever had attended Church. Rachel answered, "I have attended Church all my life. I also attend family worship at the church on Sundays. At school, we also have Daily Worship, just as you have your School Assemblies."

The Sunday School Superintendent thought to herself, "Here we have a girl aged eleven, who has attended church most of her life. Let us ask the children whether she would be suitable to serve as their May Queen this year." The children were delighted at the suggestion, and everyone heartily agreed.

On the day of the May Queen's procession, the four girls, chosen as Ladies in Waiting, wearing beautiful dresses, welcomed Rachel from Swaziland, to be their honoured May Queen. They walked down the Main Street, behind the School banner, and the County Brass band. The local Policeman led the way. He stopped the traffic to allow the procession to pass through.

The Vicar and the Priest waved and bowed to the May Queen, and her four Ladies. Everyone agreed that the choice of Queen, had been the best of any year yet. Rachel was ever so happy. She was loved by all the children of the village. The sun came out and shone all day, as if it was pleased with the event.

Rachel was glad that she had paid a visit to Britain, and that she had met the British children. She said that she would never forget being their May Queen, because the British children had chosen her themselves. After the Nurse's six months leave of absence was finished, Rachel went back with her again to Swaziland. The village children were sorry to bid them "Good-bye".

Prayer:

> Father of every land and nation,
> we thank you for your church
> and its membership around the world.
> May we always keep a welcome in our hearts,
> for all God's people.
> Bless and care for all children,
> who have lost a parent.   Amen.

Hymn:

> There are hundreds of sparrows, thousands, millions. (C&P.1. 15)
> or, Children of Jerusalem. (JP. 24)

Teachers' Note: The point here is to welcome other people, of a different racial origin. (1) Rachel's parents had died, yet God was still her Heavenly Father. (2) Many missionaries work in schools, hospitals, and churches around the world. The members of these new churches are our Christian brothers and sisters. (3) The Bible tells us that we are to welcome strangers, and offer them hospitality, and friendship.

(c) Peter's Mobile Phone   *Week 2   Leadership*

One of the twelve Apostles, whom Jesus had chosen had a nick-name. His real name was "Simon" but he was better known as "Peter. This name, Peter, means "A rock". So Peter who in the past had been a fisherman, was a very strong kind of person. He was strong as a rock. Peter was a married man. We know this because the Bible tells us that his wife's mother fell ill with a fever. Jesus touched her hand, and the fever left her. He had made her better. She was completely cured that day. (Ref. Matthew Ch.8 verse 14, and Luke 4 verse 38).

Yet when Peter was tested he failed. When Jesus had been arrested by the Roman soldiers, and three people asked Peter whether he was a disciple of Jesus, Peter denied it three times. Peter was just like any other human being, he was afraid that day that the Roman soldiers might put him into prison too. Later, after Jesus arose from the dead, Peter became a strong leader for the other Apostles. He was crucified upside down in the city of Rome.

Here is another story about a boy whose name was Peter. This was his real name, it was not a nick-name. Peter lived in Leeds. Peter's uncle James and aunt Rose had come on a visit from Australia, to visit Peter's family. They had bought Peter a mobile phone for his birthday. Peter could always phone home when he was at school, and ask his mother what was for tea that day. He loved sausages and chips as the best of all his meals.

When the school organised a weekend at the seaside, Peter brought his mobile phone with him. Mr. Hall one of the Teachers was the leader of Peter's group. There were eight children in each group. Mr. Hall drove them to the seaside in the school mini-bus. They slept overnight in a school in the seaside town. as everything had been arranged for them.

Mr. Hall took the eight children across the bay in a motor-launch to a deserted island. He suggested that they walk around the island, and come back for teatime to the little harbour. They would then take the motor-launch back across the bay, to the town school again. It was a beautiful island they had come to visit.

Mr. Hall also carried a mobile phone, and it began to ring inside his pocket. It was the police phoning across the bay, telling Mr. Hall that someone had broken the window of his school mini-bus, which he had left on the car park. Mr. Hall decided that he would take the motor-launch back across the bay, as it only took ten minutes. He explained the matter to the eight children.

He said, "This is an emergency. Now I am appointing Peter to be Leader for an hour in my place. I will get back in an hour or so, to take you back on the motor-launch again." and off he went. Peter felt a great responsibility upon his shoulders. He was now the Leader. All the children had brought strong shoes, anoraks, or wind breaking raincoats. Hoods were attached to their anoraks.

Peter led the group a walk around the beautiful lonely island. It took nearly three hours. Then something happened which frightened everyone. A sea-fret which is rather like a sea fog, began to gather. After the first hour, it became so dense, that the children could not see where they were going. Peter became very calm indeed. He told the children to stop walking round the island, and they all would go down on to the sandy shore, to look for a hut, to stay inside it, out of the cold.

He telephoned Mr. Hall, and the Teacher explained that he dare not bring the motor-boat back over the sea, because the sea-fret was so dense. "Do your best to find somewhere to stay the night." he told Peter. "Use your tents if you must." The voice on the mobile phone faded away. The sea-fog now became very thick. Very little could be seen. The children were alone on a desert island.

Peter told the group that the important thing was to keep together. Inside himself, he was beginning to feel afraid. Yet he knew that as leader, he must not show any fear and frighten the other children. Down on the shore, Peter looked at a small nearby hill, and he thought that he saw a hole in the rock. The children climbed up, to see what looked like a small smuggler's cave.

Peter said to the others, "We shall need to sleep here overnight. This is a real adventure we are having." The children took out their sandwiches, and they shared them with each other, drinking the tea and coffee from their flasks. Peter said, I could send out an S.O.S. on my mobile phone, but I will not do such a thing, until the morning. We are not really in danger here."

That night seemed to be a very dark one, and a very long one. Then the moon began to shine into the cave where they were lying. They all fell asleep. They awoke early next morning. Everyone was calm, as they washed themselves in a flowing stream, which ran down the hillside. The cold air made them very hungry.

Peter then rang his mobile phone, and Mr. Hall answered. There is a stiff breeze blowing. It will blow the fret away in about an hour. I will come over in the motor launch. The helicopter station has been informed, just in case it is needed.

Soon the children heard the sound of the motor-launch engine as it approached the island. The sea-fret had gone. Mr. Hall said, "Peter remains Leader, until we reach the other shore." Peter sat in front of the boat, until they safely reached the sandy bay again. He stood up, and said, "I am handing over Leadership to you Mr. Hall. Thank you Sir." Peter asked "What is for breakfast?" Mr. Hall shouted back, "You all may have sausages and chips this morning". The children gave three cheers for Peter.

Emergencies often happen. It is good to be a trained Leader, and not to panic.

Prayer:

> Lord, we thank you for the Apostle Peter.
> Help us first to learn self control.
> Help us to learn how to lead others.
> Show us us what makes a good leader.
> We thank you for our Leaders in school.
> May we give them due respect and attention.   Amen.

Hymn:

> By brother sun who brings the day. (C&P.2. 78)
> or, There's a child in the streets. (C&P.1. 27)

Teachers' Note: (1) Peter became a good Leader. (2) There are emergencies in life. We must be ready for these emergencies.

(a) The New Baby

Week 3   Children

Gavin was the only son of a happy family. He had a good Mum and Dad who rather spoiled him, by giving to him, toys, gifts, sports clothes, and plenty of pocket money. Anything that he particularly wanted, his parents would buy for him. When he wanted a mountain bike, Dad just bought it for him. Gavin was a very fortunate boy because he was the only son in the family.

When Gavin was about ten years old, his Mum and Dad one evening called him to give him some special news. His Mum said, "Gavin, I have special news for you. I am going to have a baby in about seven months time. Your Dad is very pleased about the news. Won't it be wonderful to have a little brother to play with?" Gavin did not say anything at that moment. He just walked away into the garden.

Gavin thought to himself, "If I have a little brother, then I will not get all the good things that my parents will buy. It means that if there are two brothers, then I shall only get one half of what I had before. It means that I will need to share everything I own with my little brother. Oh no, I prefer to get everything for myself, rather than share it with a little brother. I am not pleased with the arrival of this new baby at all."

He went out of the garden, back into the living room, to tell his Mum and Dad. Gavin said, "I have been happy by myself for ten years in this house, why should I welcome a little baby brother. I don't want to know about the new baby. I want my Mum and Dad's love all for myself."

Gavin was very angry when Mum bought new baby clothes and put them into a special drawer. Mum had chosen six months beforehand, the name of "Alister James" for the new baby. Dad arrived home one evening with a brand new baby cradle. Gavin just scowled, and pretended not to notice it. Under his breath, he said to himself, "I do not want a baby brother, because he will spoil my fun." The remaining seven months of waiting time passed by very quickly, and then Mum had to go into hospital. Gavin was really worried, because he was afraid that his Mum might die, and he would have no-one to tuck him into bed at night. Dad seemed to be worried also, as he paced up and down the floor at home. He visited Mum three evenings in the hospital.

One afternoon the telephone rang. Gavin's Aunt answered. Dad was ringing to tell them that Mum had given birth to her new baby, which was eight pounds in weight. He said that Mum and the baby were doing well. Dad said that they had a problem, and that Gavin would need to come up to the hospital, to help out with the problem. Dad would come home to collect him, and both of them could visit Mum in the hospital. Gavin could hardly wait to see his Mum again. He wondered what the problem could be.

Dad and Gavin entered the maternity ward, and there was Mum nursing a baby in her arms. Gavin looked at the baby. It had a bald head, and a face like a little old man. Mum and Dad then explained the problem. "Gavin," they explained, "our new baby is a little girl, and we did not decide on a girl's name beforehand.

Can you think of a good name for your little sister." Gavin could not believe his ears, They were asking him to give a name to the new baby.

He thought hard, and then he suggested, "How about, Helen, Mary." Mum and Dad smiled, "What a lovely name, indeed, Helen Mary. It just suits your little sister. Do we all agree then, she is to be called Helen Mary". Dad, Mum, and Gavin all agreed. Three days passed, and Mum brought the new baby home. Gavin looked at her very closely. The baby had changed. She no longer looked like a little old man with a bald head. She looked beautiful, when she opened her little eyes.

Gavin thought, "How fortunate I am to have such a beautiful baby sister, with blue eyes. How happy I am to have such a good Mum and Dad." Gavin thought to himself that having a baby sister was better than having a mountain bike. Some weeks later, the baby wrapped its tiny hands around Gavin's finger, and gripped it tightly.

Gavin was delighted. He thought again, "How silly I was, not to want a new baby. God has been good to our family. Instead of being three, we are now four."

Prayer:

> Heavenly Father, we thank you
> for every new-born baby.
> We thank you for the skill of Doctors and Nurses.
> Bless all handicapped children.
> Help us all to love and care for each other.   Amen.

Hymn:

> As I went riding by. (C&P.2. 120)
> or, Born in the night, Mary's child. (JP. 313)

Teachers' Note: (1) We all were babies at one time. A baby is beautiful. A baby is helpless. A baby is dependent. A baby is a gift from God. (2) Mothers and Dads are full of love for their children. (3) Children do not get any less love from their parents because a baby is born. Brothers and sisters can help to give love to a new baby. Later, Mum will take little Helen Mary to Church to be baptised, and to receive her Christian names.

(b) The Japanese Jug   *Week 3   Children*

Older people are always warning young people to beware of accidents. When Helen Butterworth ran across the road, the Lollipop Lady became very displeased, because she knew that Helen could have been knocked down by a car. When John Briggs pushed a younger boy into the swimming pool, the Pool

Attendant became very angry, because he knew that this foolish action could have caused a younger child to drown.

Then there are accidents in the school, at home, or in the countryside. Jesus once referred to a tragic accident. He recalled that a tower building in the city of Silom had collapsed, and that eighteen people had been killed, in that accident. Jesus said that because someone has been injured in such an accident, it does not mean that the injured people had been bad people. Good people also may be involved in an accident. Therefore we all must take care to avoid accidents.

Aunt Mary had a beautiful Japanese jug, which was about one-half metre high. She valued the jug very much, because it had been left to her by her Grandfather, who had been a Captain of a sailing ship many years ago. Aunt Mary used to dust her beloved jug almost every day, when she was polishing the piano in the parlour. Andrew and Alison, aged 9 and 11 years, were learning to play the piano, so they used to come to Aunt Mary's house, to practise on her piano.

They brought their music book along with them, and when Alison was practising her music, Andrew would amuse himself by looking inside the jug. Aunt Mary often hid little surprise gifts for the children inside the jug, because the jug was quite large. On this occasion Alison was playing "Bobby Shafto's gone to sea." Andrew took the Japanese jug into his hands and looked inside it.

Sure enough. there were two chocolate Bounty Bars inside it. Andrew, interrupted Alison's music session, by showing to her, the chocolates inside the jug. "Look" he said, Aunt Mary has put this chocolate inside, as a surprise for both of us.

Andrew passed the jug to Alison, just as she was trying to turn a page of her music. Alison fumbled as she tried to catch the jug in one hand. The precious jug slipped from her hand, and fell. Horror of horrors, the jug hit the brass foot of the piano, and then bounced against the radiator, and shattered into pieces on the floor. Andrew and Alison were shocked! They had broken Aunt Mary's antique jug! What could they do? They could never stick it together again.

Aunt Mary was making a cup of tea for the children in the kitchen, when she heard the crash. She rushed into the parlour, and caught sight of her jug in pieces lying on the carpet. "It was an accident, Aunt Mary," Alison shouted. "It just happened."

"It really was an accident," cried out Andrew. Aunt Mary was sobbing. Big tears were running down her face. She really loved that Japanese jug. "Oh what shall I do" she moaned.

Alison turned to her music book to find something, which she could play, to calm Aunt Matilda down. She played the first music on the page, and it turned out to be,

Humpty Dumpty sat on the wall.
Humpty Dumpty had a great fall.
All the king's horses, and all the king's men,
Could not put Humpty together again.

When Alison realised what music she was playing, she stopped, but Aunt Mary was laughing as if she could not stop. "Humpty Dumpty, indeed. What a suitable piece of music to play at a time like this! Ha, ha, ha, he, he, he! We shall never put that jug together again. Ha, ha, ha, he, he. It is no use crying over spilt milk. It really was only a very old jug." she said.

She was still laughing. Both the children realised that Aunt Mary was not angry after all. "Oh do not worry about that old Japanese jug, children," she said. "I shall not have to dust it any more. It has all been an accident! I am sure that you children did not break it on purpose."

Andrew and Alison were relieved. They finished practising their music pieces rather early that evening. As they were going out the door, homewards, Aunt Mary said, "Children, are you not forgetting something? Here are the two surprise Bounty Bars, which were inside the jug." Andrew and Alison thought that Aunt Mary was a very kind lady. After all, it really had been an accident. What Aunt Mary had shown, was that she loved Andrew and Alison, much more than she loved her Japanese jug.

The children determined that they would not meddle with other people's property again. Accidents happen so easily. Not everyone would be so forgiving, as their Aunt Mary.

Prayer:

We thank you, Lord, our Heavenly Father,
that when we make mistakes, that you forgive us.
Teach us that when other people
accidentally offend us,
that we shall not take it to heart.
Give us a forgiving spirit at all times.   Amen.

Hymn:

I belong to a family, the biggest on earth. (C&P.1. 69)

Teachers Note: (1) Life is sometimes littered with accidents. We must try to avoid accidents, by taking special care. (2) If someone accidentally upsets us by the things they do or say, let us always forgive them. (3) We may pray for anyone whom we know, who has had an accident in their life.

(c) Ben's Lunch

We do not know this boy's real name, so we shall invent a name, and call him "Benjamin." He would be known to his young friends as "Ben." He lived in a stone house near the Sea of Galilee. He saw crowds of people whom he knew lived on the other side of the Sea of Galilee. They had come over to his side of the inland sea. They were following a famous healer, who preached to the people, and did miracles before their eyes.

Ben ran into his mother, who was in the kitchen. "Mum, I am going to see the famous healer and Teacher. Thousands of people are going. Please, Mum, make me up a good lunch, because I shall be away all day."

Ben's mother knew that Ben could be a very hungry boy just before meal times. She made him a packed lunch, of five little round home-baked barley loaves, and she cooked two small fishes. She carefully packed the lunch in a cloth napkin to keep it cool and fresh. Ben thanked his mother, and off he went to see the Healer, whose name was, "Jesus".

About five thousand people had gathered to hear what the healer had to say. After a long day of hearing Jesus teaching, one of the twelve special followers of the Healer, named Philip, said to Jesus, "Where can we buy bread to feed such a large crowd of people? Where would the money come from to pay for feeding so many people."

Another of the Healer's disciples named Andrew, noticed Ben carrying his lunch, wrapped up in a napkin. Andrew talked to Ben, and brought him to Jesus the Healer. Andrew said to Jesus, "See, here is a boy with a packed lunch. He has five small round barley loaves and two small fishes. What use would they be to feed such a crowd?"

Jesus told the disciples to tell the people to sit down on the green grass. When they counted the numbers of people, there were five thousand sitting on the grass. Jesus took Ben's lunch in his hands, and he said Grace over the five small round loaves and two small fishes. Jesus then gave the loaves and fishes to his twelve disciples, and he told them to distribute Ben's lunch to the people.

The disciples gave out the bread and fishes to the people who were sitting down. The more they gave away, the more they seemed to have. They distributed the food to the five thousand people, until everyone was satisfied. A miracle was happening before their very eyes. When everyone had eaten, Jesus told his disciples to gather up the remaining fragments, so that there would be no waste.

The disciples carefully gathered up the remaining fragments lying about, and the fragments filled twelve baskets. When the people saw the miracle for themselves, they thought, "let us take this man Jesus, and we will make him our king. We need never be hungry again." However, when Jesus knew that they might take him by force to make him a king, he quietly escaped from the crowd, and went to a mountain, just to be alone.

The twelve disciples walked towards the seashore again. The twelve men embarked on a fishing vessel, and sailed back again over the Sea of Galilee. As they were near the shore, they saw someone walking towards them, as if he was walking on the water. As he approached the boat, the disciples were afraid. Jesus saw how fearful they were, so he shouted out, "Don't be afraid, it is I."

They received him into the boat, and just at that moment, the boat had reached dry land. They had arrived at the end of their journey. Ben rushed home to tell his mother about the miracle of his lunch, and his wonderful adventure.

Just think to yourself. "If you had been there on that day, would you have been willing to share your lunch with Jesus? Have you ever shared anything, with anyone else?"

Prayer:

> Lord God, our heavenly Father,
> We are thankful that we are not hungry.
> We earnestly pray for all hungry men, women,
> and children from the third world countries.
> We pray for the poor families of our own country.
> Bless us all with good harvests.   Amen.

Hymn:

> I saw a man from Galilee. (C&P.2. 75)
> or, Now the harvest is all gathered. (C&P.2. 139)

Teachers' Note: (1) Ben's lunch belonged to Ben, but he freely gave it to Jesus. (2) Notice that Jesus said grace over Ben's lunch. This means he thanked God for the food. (3) Jesus gave the food to the disciples, and they in turn gave it to the people. We must never forget that when we eat, that our food has already passed through the hands of other people. Ref. John Chap. 6. verses 1-20.

(a) Mother Susanna

Week 4   Mothers

This Assembly is about Susanna Wesley, the mother of John and Charles Wesley. The story of John Wesley's rescue from the fire is found on page 12 of Book number one, "Tell us a Story." However, the fire was also part of Susanna's experience, and for that reason it is included here.

Susanna Wesley was the mother of nineteen children. She was the wife of a Church of England Rector, the Rev. Samuel Wesley, who came to Epworth village in the year in 1697. During the 17th. and the 18th. Centuries, children did not live very long. Many of them died of various diseases as babies before the age of five years.

So, when we say that Susanna had nineteen children, we also must say that only ten lived, and that the other nine died when they were infants They were buried in Epworth church-yard. Of the ten children who lived, seven were girls, and three were boys. Their Rectory was a large house, in wet fenland, (marshy ground) some distance from Doncaster.

The children had plenty of room for playing in such a large house. Susanna was a good wife to her husband, and a good mother to her family. The children did not go to school, when they were very young, but they were educated by their mother, Susanna, in the kitchen. When each child reached the age of five years, Susanna taught them separately to master the alphabet. This only took one day, (except for Mollie and Anne, who took one and a half days to learn it).

The next step was to teach each child to read. Susanna did this, by getting the children to begin reading the Book of Genesis chapter 1, verse 1. So, in the Rectory kitchen the children were taught reading, and writing, from ten o'clock until twelve o'clock in the morning, and from two o'clock to four o'clock in the afternoon.

Susanna, also spent a private session with each of her children separately, when she taught them their own private religious duties. This involved saying the Lord's Prayer, and knowing the Ten Commandments, and other important Church matters. She taught each child to ask God for forgiveness, if they did some wrong deed.

We cannot tell the story of Susanna Wesley, without at least mentioning February ninth, 1709, when one cold night, the Rectory went on fire. Susanna being a good mother, rushed to waken the children and the maids, and little baby Samuel. They were all rescued, and stood outside on the lawn in the darkness to watch the men trying to put out the fire. In the garden the Rector gathered his family around him. Suddenly, someone shouted, "Where is Jackie ?" (John, was then known as "Jackie", who then was aged seven). Jackie sleeping alone, had been wakened by all the noise, and crackling of the flames. He opened the upstairs window, and put his little head out to see what was happening.

The crowd standing on the lawn saw the boy, and also saw the flames leaping higher behind him in the house. The rescuers had no ladder long enough at the time, so one man climbed on the shoulders of a second man, until they reached the widow sill. They pulled Jackie through the window, and passed him down to the ground, and away from the burning building.

Susanna cuddled the little boy close to her. He knew that he was safe. John Wesley dearly loved his mother. He cuddled in close to her. The flames burnt so highly, that the Rectory roof caved in, amid a mass of flames and sparks.

Eventually the villagers helped to put out the fire. The Rector knelt down on his knees, and thanked God for saving every member of his family.

After the fire, Susanna believed that God had saved Jackie from certain death in the fire. He was "as a brand plucked from the burning" for some special purpose. (A "brand" is a piece of partly burning wood. This saying means that Jackie Wesley was just like a piece of burning wood plucked out of the fire.)

The Rectory was rebuilt, and the Wesley family moved in again. The children were taught by Susanna to be respectful to each other. When speaking to each other, in the family, they would say, "Sister Hetty," or "Brother John". To us, this kind of conversation with each other, sounds rather quaint, but Susanna wanted her family to know good manners, even to each other.

Susanna, did not mind the stacks of books piled up here and there in the Rectory, although the girls objected to their Father stacking books in their wardrobe. In an age when there was no free education, Susanna knew that children who loved books, would reap success in their lives. The children were good readers.

The Wesley family had a very loving Mother. Susanna was not just the mother of the Wesley family. She was a good devout Anglican Christian. She became mother of the later world-wide Methodist Churches, by her influence upon her middle son, "John". Another brother, Charles, became a famous poet and a musician. Even when John was older, he often asked his mother's advice, and accepted her guidance at times.

Prayer:

> Lord, we thank you for kind mothers.
> We thank you for Susanna Wesley,
> and for her love for her children.
> We thank you for Hannah the mother of Samuel,
> and for Mary the mother of Jesus.   Amen.

Hymn:

> Give me oil in my lamp, keep me burning. (C&P.1. 43), (JP. 50)

Teachers' Note: (1) This story is a little glimpse into family life during the eighteenth century. (2) Susanna was the daughter of the Rev. Dr. Samuel Annesley, once a Lecturer of St. Paul's London. Susanna gained much of her depth of character from her father. (3) Children should understand that Susanna and the Wesley family lived before the days of National education. (Methodists today, often address each other naturally as, "Sister," or "Brother," without thought).

(b) Mother Cat

Flossie was a beautiful grey she-cat. She lived in a high residential building in the city of New York. Her owner was a lady, who lived on the ninth floor. The lady took very good care of her cat, and fed it well, because she loved it so much. The Lady had to go to work every day, but she had employed a carpenter to make a small square "Cat Flap" on swinging hinges, in her front door.

This meant that the cat could always come home for a drink of milk, or some cat-food at any time of the day. Flossie knew that if she pressed the cat-flap with her head, that it would swing open, and that she could pass through into the lady's apartment.

One day, Flossie gave birth to seven lovely little kittens. The lady put the kittens in a cardboard box, and put soft newspapers underneath them, so that the box could always be kept clean. As the seven kittens grew a little larger, more milk and more cat-food was always left for their dinner. The Lady was very happy, and Flossie the mother cat was also very happy. Indeed, Flossie was very proud of her kittens.

When Flossie needed a walk in the fresh air, even at night, she went out through the cat-flap, and down the eight flights of stairs to the back of the buildings. However, the kittens, were too young to venture far, so they remained in their cosy cardboard box, eight floors up, in the lady's apartment.

One eventful day, when the cat's owner was away at her place of work, she had forgotten to switch off the electric fire. The cloth fringe around her big settee became hotter, and hotter, until it burst into flames. This electric fire had set the flat on fire. The people who lived on the same landing, smelt the smoke, and 'phoned for the fire brigade, which arrived within minutes.

Smoke was pouring out of the windows, and along the corridors. The loud sounds of more sirens of fire-engines and police cars came to Flossie, as she prowled along the street. She instantly remembered that she was a mother-cat. Flossie, sprang up the stairs three at a time, past first, and second floors, and onward, up to the ninth floor of the building. She rushed through the cat-flap and went up to the cardboard box, where her kittens lay, coughing in the smoke.

She picked up one of them by the scruff of the neck, and carried it quickly through the cat-flap, and down eight flights of stairs, to an old coal bunker, on the ground floor. She put the kitten in the coal bunker, and ran back again, up the eight flights of stairs, to collect another kitten. She heard the firemen breaking in the windows because the building was very high.

Flossie carried the second kitten in her teeth, down to safety. The firemen were hosing the rooms by now. Flossie picked up a third kitten, and carried it also to safety, through the cat-door. Like a good mother, Flossie did not rest, until she had carried all her seven kittens down to the safety of the coal bunker on the ground floor.

The lady owner of the flat arrived back, with her keys, to open the door for the firemen. Everything inside had been singed or burned by the flames. When she looked for the cardboard box, it had been burned up. No cat or kittens remained. The Owner thought that the cats had all been killed in the fire. She was truly sorry that she had left the electric fire switched "on" instead of "off."

The firemen soon cleaned up the mess caused by the fire and smoke. The lady ordered some new furniture, and it was supplied immediately. The house-decorators were to come next morning, to re-decorate the inside walls of the house, and to fit new windows.

Two policemen were amazed to see, Flossie the mother-cat, carry her seven kittens back up the stairs, and through the little cat-flap into the room again. The Lady was delighted that her cat and kittens were safe. She found another cardboard box for them to lie in. One of the two policemen, who had been watching Flossie said, "There is the bravest mother in the city of New York."

Prayer:

> Heavenly Father, we thank you for motherhood.
> We are grateful that we have homes, and families.
> Teach us to take care of our school.
> Bless all our Teachers, and our school friends.
> We pray for people who have no homes.   Amen.

Hymn:

> Have you seen the pussycat, sitting on the wall? (JP. 72)
> or, All the animals I have ever seen. (C&P.2. 80)

Teachers' Note: (1) Flossie was a good mother-cat, because she took care of her kittens. (2) We should never be careless about fire-risks. (3) Flossie was brave and wise enough to get her kittens out of the dangerous smoke and flames. We need brave fire-officers and police-officers in emergencies.

(c) Jesus and the Children

Week 4   Mothers

Jesus was kept very busy, preaching to the people, teaching his Disciples, and healing the sick and disabled people. One day, Jesus was speaking to a crowd of adults. The mothers were gathered with their little children in their arms, and some of the children were clinging to their mother's skirts. They were very interested, in hearing what Jesus had to say.

The Disciples knew that Jesus was often tired, after dealing with people all day long. The mothers had brought their children to Jesus, so that he could give them a special blessing. The Disciples scolded the mothers, and told them to go away off home.

Jesus saw what was happening. Immediately he stopped the Disciples driving the children away. He spoke very kindly to them. "Please, do not send the children away. Allow them to come to me. These children are members of my kingdom. Children are trustful, loving and believing. Allow them to come near."

Jesus lifted the children in his arms. He gathered them around his knee, and he sat some of them upon his lap. It was plain for all to see, that he really loved the children. Then, Jesus turned round and looked at the older people, and he became very stern. He said that if anyone harmed a little child, that it would be better for that evil person, if he were cast into the deepest sea and drowned.

Here is another little story. The Under-Five-year olds were allowed to sit in church by themselves, because it was "Mothering Sunday" The older children called the day, "Mothers Day," but the Minister explained that it was the Church who was "Mother" on this Sunday, and that children were always welcome.

The mothers were very anxious about allowing their children to sit with the other children in the pews, because they were inclined to make such a noise and hub-bub No-one seemed to mind, since this was a special day in the church calendar. The hymns were easy hymns to sing, and the sermon and prayers were very short that Sunday morning. Then, several ladies appeared with large trays of flowers. They stood at the front of the Church. The children queued up in a long line, and each boy and girl received a little bunch of flowers.

Each child was allowed to walk anywhere in the Church, and to present their own mother with the bunch of flowers. They were full of excitement. The mothers were ever so proud to receive flowers from their own children. The Minister and grown-up people all smiled very pleasantly.

Then they sang the same beloved hymn, which they seemed to sing every year. They sang:

> When mothers of Salem,
> their children brought to Jesus.
> The stern Disciples drove them back,
> and bid them all depart.
> But Jesus saw them e're they fled,
> and sweetly smiled, and kindly said,
> Suffer the children to come unto me.

> William Medlen Hutchings, (1827-76)

The children all went home that Sunday morning, very happy indeed. They began to understand that they were acting out, the previously told Bible story, of Jesus and the Children.

Prayer:

> Heavenly Father, we thank you that Jesus
> loves all children everywhere.
> We admire his kindness and patience.
> Bless our mothers, and guardians,
> who take care of us.
> Bless and protect all needy children.   Amen.

Hymn:

> The ink is black, the page is white. (C&P.1.)

Teachers' Note: (1) In these days of broken marriages, families may become extended families. Great care is needed in speaking to children, to accept families and parents as they now exist. (2) Jesus had time for children. He loved children. This is very important for a child to know, and believe. (3) The Christian Church is like a Mother who has a place for all her children. References: See Matthew 19, Mark 10, and Luke 18.

(a) Greyfriar's Bobby   *Week 5   Friendship*

Most Scottish children have heard in school, and in Church, the true story of Greyfriar's Bobby, the little Skye Terrier. Teachers, Ministers, and Priests have often told the account of the faithful little Shepherd dog named Bobby. He lived during the reign of Queen Victoria. The dog's owner was known as Old Jock, who had been a shepherd on the Scottish hillsides. In time, old Jock's wife had died, and Bobby the Skye Terrier, and old Jock became very loving friends.

When Jock became old, he had to leave his country life, and the sheep behind him. He found a room on the fifth floor of a tenement in the City of Edinburgh. Tenements in those days, were like old fashioned high rise flats. A family had to share one or two rooms, known as "A butt and ben." Old Jock brought his beloved little Bobby with him, hidden in his large Shepherd-coat pocket.

Everyone knew that when the Castle fired the gun that it is one-o'clock, and time for dinner. Bobby the dog, became used to the noise caused by the firing of the Castle gun. When the gun fired, Bobby also knew it was dinner time. Old Jock and the little dog would descend the five flights of stairs, and go to the Old Greyfriars Cafe for his dinner. The old Shepherd always shared his dinner with Bobby. The kind owner of the Dining Rooms became such a friend of the dog, that he provided a special tin plate, for the dog to eat out of, while Old Jock also was eating his dinner.

Bobby and Old Jock would walk back to the lodgings, and climb the stairs again. In his room, often Old Jock would open his Bible. He loved to read the twenty-third Psalm. "The Lord is my Shepherd, I shall not want." Old Jock understood and loved these words.

Old Jock had a bad cough, and as the years went by, he became very ill. Then one sad day, Old Jock died. The Funeral Directors came and put Old Jock in his coffin. They took him away. Bobby the little dog, kept out of the way, but he was clever enough to follow the funeral. The coffin was taken to Greyfriars Churchyard. Soon, the funeral was completed, and Old Jock was buried. Outside Greyfriars Churchyard, was a painted sign, "No dogs allowed."

When the people had gone home, Bobby crawled under the gates, and smelt his way back to Old Jock's grave. Bobby lay down on top of the grave, and went to sleep. All at once, he heard the boom of the Castle gun firing. Bobby ran out of the graveyard, and as usual, he went in to the Dining Rooms. The Owner of the Dining Rooms provided the little dog with his hot dinner, and off he went again, back to the grave. He never went back to the rooms in the Edinburgh tenement. He always returned and slept on Old Jock's grave. Each day, when the Castle gun fired, he toddled into the Dining Rooms once more for his dinner.

The Edinburgh Newspaper Editors heard about faithful little Bobby, so they paid for a little dog-kennel to be built on top of Old Jock's grave. Bobby became knows as "Greyfriars Bobby." He lived for fourteen years, until he also became old. Then the little dog also died. The officials at the Churchyard decided that they would break the graveyard rules, just once. So they buried Greyfriars Bobby in the same grave as old Jock. So, that even in their deaths, master and dog were not divided.

If you ever get the opportunity, to visit Edinburgh, be sure to ask to see the Greyfriars Churchyard for yourself. Look for Bobby's Statue and the bronze fountain, as you go in the gate. Even Queen Victoria later came to visit the little Dog's monument. Everyone in Edinburgh loved the true story of Greyfriars Bobby. Many people would have given the little dog a good home, but Bobby always came back to lie on his master's grave, even if he was taken miles away, he always found his way back. People in Edinburgh tell the story in their own way, just as if Bobby was their own little four-footed friend.

Prayer:

> We thank you Lord, for the faithful love of our pets.
> Father God, we thank you for the world of nature.
> We are glad to live in an environment of trees,
> flowers, fields, rivers, and mountains.   Amen.

Hymn:

The Lord is my Shepherd, I shall not want. (C&P.1. 56), (J.P. 243)

Teachers' Note: (1) Old Jock had a faithful friend in his little Skye Terrier. It is good to care for pets, but we must remember that animals are not toys to be thrown away, when we tire of them. (2) Old Jock found comfort through reading the Twenty-third Psalm. (3) Fourteen years is a long time for a dog to sit on his master's grave. Greyfriar's Bobby is a good example of faithful friendship.

(b) Two Good Friends   *Week 5   Friendship*

Today, you have to imagine that you are a Judge in a Court. You are to listen carefully to a story, which may have happened during the days when King John ruled England. King John ruled in place of King Richard the Lion-heart, who was away overseas fighting. You are to decide which were wrong actions, and which were good actions. The story is about friendship.

In the old legends, Robin Hood and Little John were very good friends. Robin was an expert bow-man with the long-bow. He could shoot a duck flying in the air, or a wolf, or a wild boar creeping in the forest. His friend, Little John, was a huge man, and very strong. Little John was also a good bow-man, but Little John was the best fighter with the quarter-staff, which was a thick pole, made from a black-thorn hedge branch. All this happened in the days before guns were invented. Robin Hood and his merry men, lived in Sherwood forest. It is said that they robbed the rich, and gave what they stole to the hungry poor.

One day, Robin and Little John were arguing about something, and the argument became so heated, that Little John just walked away. He, being a man of war, never liked arguing with Robin Hood his leader. Little John walked towards Nottingham. Unfortunately, he was captured that day by the Sheriff of Nottingham, and a small company of soldiers, who tied Little John to a tree.

Robin Hood had also been sorry that he had begun the argument with his good friend. While walking through the trees, Robin suddenly met Guy of Gisborne, riding his horse along a forest path. Guy had declared that he would kill Robin Hood the first time he met him, because Robin was an enemy of the Sheriff of Nottingham.

These two expert bow-men confronted each other, and fought a two-man battle with their swords. Robin Hood was a good swordsman. He killed Guy of Gisborne. He then took Guy's horse, and rode as fast as he could through the forest looking for his friend, Little John. Suddenly, he came across the Sheriff of Nottingham with his soldiers, guarding Little John, whom they had tied to a tree.

The Sheriff did not know Robin Hood, and he actually mis-took Robin for Guy of Gisborne, (who was now dead). So, he gave Little John into the custody of Robin Hood. Robin and Little John were carrying their own bows. Both men turned together, and used their bows and arrows with such accuracy, that they frightened off, the Sheriff and his soldiers. Very quietly both Little John and Robin Hood jumped on two horses, which were tethered to a tree nearby, and galloped away into the safety of the green-leafed cover of Sherwood Forest.

The two friends decided that they would never argue against each other with such force again. Little John said to Robin, "It is better to lose an argument, than to lose a friend." Robin said to Little John, "A friend in need, is a friend indeed."

Now for the verdicts. These are very difficult questions.

(1)   Is an argument between friends a good thing?

(2)   Is it right or wrong to steal from the rich to give it to the poor? Say why.

(3)   Do you think that discussion is a better way to solve problems, than using swords, quarter-staffs, and bows and arrows? Say why?

(4)   Do you think that good King Richard the Lion-heart would have done better to remain in England, in order to see that his people were having fair play.

(5)   Did you find it difficult trying to be a Judge, and deciding these problems?

Prayer:

  Lord, life has many problems, even for children.
  Teach us the way of peace and understanding.
  Bless all poor and hungry people.
  Bring wars and quarrels to an end, everywhere.
  Make us more like Jesus, the Prince of Peace.   Amen.

Hymn:

  Think of all the things we lose. (C&P.1. 57)

Teachers' Note: (1) Legends were told down the ages, from person to person. Often they are changed in their telling. (2) Robin Hood was a popular hero, because people believed him to have been a good man. Many stories are about a clash between good and evil. (3) Human friends are something special in life.

(c) A Friend at Mid-Night   *Week 5   Friendship*

Jesus was explaining why people pray. He told this story. There were once two good friends. Both of their families lived in houses in the same street. A poor man's house in those days, was only a small square type building, with holes in the wall for windows. A little higher than the families' heads, there was a part of the ceiling, which was really a loft. Families slept up there together; each person rolled up in a separate blanket. When the door of the house was shut, that meant that everyone was up in the ceiling loft, fast asleep.

The second man, whom we shall call "the Host," had a guest arrive at his house, very late at night. Now the Host had no bread in his house, to give his guest a meal. So he quietly went outside of his own house, and went down the street, to the home of his best friend. It was mid-night, and the door was shut, and everything was in darkness.

The Host rapped his friend's door very loudly, and wakened him up out of his sleep. He shouted in the window to him, "Help me out, my friend. I have had a visitor, who has just arrived at my house, after a journey. He is to to stay overnight. I have no food in the house. Please, lend me three loaves." (These loaves were small loaves rather like baps or bannocks, which are oatmeal cakes!)

The Host's best friend did not want to open the door in the darkness. He called out, "Do not bother me. My children are all in bed with me. I cannot get up now. The door is shut." However, the Host outside continued knocking, as if he were never going to stop. On and on he knocked. In the end, his best Friend had to get out of his bed, which meant rolling away his blanket. He came down from the loft, opened the door, and gave three small loaves to the man outside. The Host went home to feed his guest.

Jesus, after telling the disciples this story, said, "Because he was a friend, and because of the man's persistent knocking at the door, he came and gave him the three loaves. This is just like prayer. Ask and it shall be given you. Seek and you shall find. Knock and it shall be opened unto you."

Making praying more understandable

Prayer is sometimes just like asking. It seems so easy. The prayer is answered right away. Illustration. It just happens!

Sometimes, we have to answer our own prayers. If we seek, we shall find. If we do our part, God will do his part. Illustration. To get good results in our examinations, we must study. Praying is not enough!

Sometimes prayer is like knocking at a door. The answer to our prayer may take a longer time to come. So the answer is "Not yet." Illustration. Long ago, Christians used to pray that the selling of people as slaves would stop. It only happened after a long time of praying.

Sometimes the answer to our praying is a clear, "No." to the paticular favour for which we are praying. Illustration. A little girl who asks God for a shop-window full of cream cakes is just greedy. The answer is sure to be "NO."

Jesus is saying that God is our heavenly Father, and that he wants to answer our prayers, if they are for the good of all concerned.

Prayer:

> Lord God, our Father, we know that you
> are more willing to hear us, than we are to ask.
> Teach us to remember that when
> we are in trouble, God is our friend.
> May the prayer of thanksgiving be ours.   Amen.

Hymn:

> Our Father, who art in heaven. (C&P.1. 51), (JP. 192)

Teachers' Note: (1) Praying sometimes is very easy. (Ask). (2) Sometimes we must answer our own prayers. (Seek). It is no good praying to become a pianist, if one does not practise. (3) Sometimes answers to our prayers take a long time to come. (Maturity involves time).

(a) The School Nurse   *Week 6   Welfare*

Sandra had always wanted to be a nurse. When she was a little girl, her Dad once bought her a Nurse's uniform. He brought it home on her fifth birthday. There was a white nurse's hat. She also had a stethoscope made from plastic, and a bag of real bandages. The uniform had a blue tunic, with a white apron.

On the apron was a Red Cross. Sandra wore the apron, and set her dolls and teddy bears out on the settee. She pretended to give each doll or teddy a spoonful of medicine, which, of course, was only water on a spoon from a tumbler. She could bandage up her dolls arms or legs with real bandages, or with sticking plaster.

When Sandra grew older, and went up to the secondary school, she found that she still wanted to be a Nurse. So she worked very hard at her G.S.C.E's, and passed them with good grades. When she was eighteen, Sandra applied for entry into the Local Hospital. The Doctors and the Teaching Supervisors questioned her at the interview, about "Why she wanted to become a Nurse?" Sandra told them that she liked helping people."

It was very good news, when Sandra received a reply through the post, that she had passed her interview. For three years, she studied General Nursing. Then she spent another two years studying Children's Nursing. Next she studied Midwifery, so that she knew how to deliver babies. Finally she studied Nursing in Education Establishments. (Schools.)

At last, Sandra felt that she knew enough, to become a School Nurse. This meant that she drove her car around the schools, and inspected the childrens' condition of health. Some rude children called her "Nitty Nora" because they though that was all she did, just looking at children's heads. Other wiser children, knew that she was now a School Nurse, who knew all about children's ailments.

One hot Summer's day, Nurse Sandra visited a school on the edge of town. She inspected all their eyes, teeth, and hair. One girl named, "Diane" looked to be unwell. Nurse Sandra put a thermometer into Diane's mouth, and gently held her wrist in order to count her pulse rate. It was throbbing very fast. When Nurse Sandra looked at Diane's temperature reading on the thermometer, it was a 100 degrees. (A normal temperature is 96 degrees).

Nurse said to Diane, "Diane, you are very ill. I will telephone the Doctor, immediately. The Doctor answered the call right away and arrived in his car. He phoned for an ambulance, which whisked Diane off to hospital. She had a painful appendicitis, and had to have an immediate operation.

Nurse Sandra was glad that she was a Nurse, and that she could diagnose such illness in a school with so many pupils. The Doctor rang to thank Sandra for her care which she had taken over the school children's health. The children never called Nurse Sandra "Nitty Nora" again, because they knew that she may have saved their friend's Diane's life.

Prayer:

> Lord God, how much we owe you,
> for our continued welfare.
> We thank you for our expert Nurses
> who attend to our school health, and hygiene.
> Bless all young people who will train
> in teaching Hospitals to become Nurses.   Amen.

Hymn:

> Come and praise the Lord. (C&P.1. 20), (JP. 34)

Teachers' Note: (1) Sandra wanted to become a trained Nurse from her childhood. (2) Sandra had to work very hard at school, and then she had to study for years at the Teaching Hospital. When she reached her goal in life, and graduated with a Degree in Welfare Nursing, she was very proud indeed. (3) Nurse Sandra loved her work, and she knew that she would be helping people all her life.

(b) Rebecca's Engagement

Abram had been told by God to leave the city where he had been living and to travel to a new country, which God would give to him, and to his children forever. The new country was called "Canaan." Sometimes it was known as "the Promised Land," because God had promised it to Abram.

Many years later, God made a Covenant with Abram. The Covenant was an agreement between God and Abram. The agreement was that God would allow Sarah, Abram's wife, to have a baby, who would become the first member of a large nation of people. God then changed Abram's name to "Abraham," which means "Father of Nations." Although she was an old woman, Sarah had a lovely baby boy called "Isaac." When Isaac grew up to be a man, Abraham and the family were living in the Promised Land.

Later Sarah, Abraham's wife died. Abraham and Isaac had loved Sarah very much. When Isaac was old enough to marry, Abraham, his father, sent his most trusted servant back to his native country, where his brother lived. He did not want Isaac to marry any of the women from this new Land of Promise, because they worshiped idols. "Find me a young woman who would make a good wife for Isaac," he said to his servant.

The servant arrived in Abraham's native country after a long journey by camel. He had brought many lovely presents with him. (Gold, silver and jewels, because Abraham was very rich). This meant that he owned many cattle. They had arrived at Abraham's brother's (Nahor) village in the evening. The trusted servant made his camels kneel down beside the well. He watched the women from the village come out to the well, to draw up water.

The servant prayed to God to help him to find the right woman who would make Isaac a good wife. He decided on a method of finding the right woman He would ask one of them to to give him a drink of water. If she said, "Yes!" and offered to give water to the camels also, then she would be the right wife for Isaac.

As the servant was praying, a very beautiful young woman came to the well. She filled her own water pitcher. The servant, went forward to her, and said, "Please may I have a drink?" She replied, "Yes, Sir, and I will be pleased to draw water for your camels too. They may drink all they need." She filled the camels drinking trough over and over again, until the camels had enough to drink, after their long hot journey.

The servant offered the young woman some of the gifts which he had brought. She told him that her name was, "Rebecca." She turned out to be Isaac's cousin. The servant asked Rebecca, whether he could stay with her father's family overnight. He intended to ask her father, to allow Rebecca to marry Isaac, his master's son. The servant thanked God for helping him to find Rebecca.

Rebecca hurried home to tell the news about the arrival of Abraham's servant. She showed the family the jewellery which he had given her as a present. They were pleased to invite Abraham's servant back home to stay overnight. The family agreed, "Yes, you may take Rebecca back to Isaac, to be his wife."

Rebecca agreed to travel back at once. She brought her childhood nurse, as well as other servants with her. So they all set off on their camels travelling back to Canaan. When they arrived back at Abraham's home, Isaac just looked at Rebecca, and they both fell in love with each other immediately. They were happily married, and they both became very fond of each other. The trusted servant was also very happy that he had found the right bride for Isaac. Abraham was very pleased at how matters had worked out.

This story will help you to understand what an "arranged marriage" in the Eastern countries means. The Parents in many countries choose a bride for their son. The Bride's Father may also have to give a "Dowry," which is a marriage gift of some value, before the marriage may take place.

Prayer:

> Heavenly Father, we thank you
> for the lovely story of Rebecca and Isaac.
> We pray for every married couple,
> setting up a home.
> Bless all families, with two parents,
> and bless all those one-parent families too.   Amen.

Hymn:

> He's got the whole world in his hand. (C&P.1. 19), (JP. 78)

Teachers' Note: (1) This is an opportunity to explain the Eastern "arranged marriage." This arrangement was the Parents traditional method of providing welfare for their family. (2) Abraham's trusted servant was more than a mere servant, he was Abraham's friend. (3) The important point is that even though the marriage had been arranged, Isaac and Rebecca dearly loved each other.

(c) David's Kindness

Week 6   Welfare

King David had a very good friend, named "Jonathan". They had been close friends most of their lives. Jonathan was the son of King Saul, the first king of Israel. When King Saul was mentally ill, and wanted to kill David, Jonathan always warned David, so that he could escape in time. There was a battle at

Gilboa, and sad to say, King Saul, Jonathan and his brothers were all killed that day. David became king of Israel, in place of Saul.

David remembered that when he and Jonathan were best friends, they both had promised that they would take care of each others families, if either of them should die. King David sent for Ziba, who was an old trusted servant of King Saul's palace. David asked him, "Are there any of King Saul's household still alive? I once made a promise to take care of them." Ziba thought for a moment, then he said, "Yes. There is one of Jonathan's sons who is still alive."

Ziba went on talking, "The one son who still is living is named, "Me-phib-osheth." He could never be a soldier and fight in battles. When he was five years of age, his nurse was carrying him to safety, and she accidentally let him drop out of her arms. The little boy fell down to the stone floor. Both the boy's feet were badly injured, and afterward, he could only walk in a hobbling kind of way. He was very lame in both feet." If it had happened today, someone would have phoned for the ambulance, and the Doctors at the hospital would have operated on the boy"s feet to make him better. In those days there were no hospitals, and no ambulances. The boy grew up to be a man, but he never could walk very well.

King David had a kind heart, so he sent for Me-phib-osheth to come to his Palace. The crippled boy came and he bowed in fear, before the king. King David said, "Never be afraid of me. I was your father's best friend, when he was alive. For his sake, I want to give you back all your family's land. It shall belong to you. However, I want you to come and live with me at my palace. You need never be hungry, because you may dine with me at my table, every day. I shall always protect you, for the sake of Jonathan, your father."

King David then spoke to the family servant. David said, "Now Ziba, I have returned all Saul's land to Me-phib-osheth. He is the lawful owner. I want you, Ziba, and your family, to farm the land for Me-phib-osheth's family, so that they will have plenty of good harvests. Me-phib-osheth is the son of my best friend, Jonathan. Therefore, he shall live in my palace as my honoured guest for the rest of his life."

The point of this story is to show what welfare really means in practical terms. It shows how God through the kindness of King David, provided a home, meals, clothing, and bed, for a little fatherless crippled boy. It also shows how he put a trusted manager over the boy's farm-land, which the boy had inherited. Children should be thankful for the kind person who provides care for them. Do you know who cares for you?

Prayer:

Heavenly Father, we thank you for the kindness
of King David to a crippled boy.
We thank you for our friends, and for their families.

We thank you for everyone
who welcomed the Lord Jesus to their house.
Keep our homes happy places.   Amen.

Hymn:

Now thank we all our God. (C&P.1. 38), (JP. 175)

Teachers' Note: (1) Sometimes two people can become life-long friends, just like David and Jonathan. (2) King David felt responsibility for Jonathan's handicapped son, Me-phib-osheth. (The name may be hyphenated for easier spelling.) (3) David provided life-long security for him. For the children, the meaning of the term, "providing welfare" is providing love and care!

(a) Coin in a Fish's Mouth

Week 7   Mystery

Some of the stories that are told about Jesus in the New Testament are difficult to understand. They could be explained in different ways. Perhaps, that is why the New Testament writers took note of them, and wrote them down. Here is one such account. Here is a story about Jesus, listen very carefully, and then see whether you can say what the story means.

After Jesus and his disciples had arrived back to the village of Ca-per-na-um, which was on the West side of the Lake of Galilee, several Tax Collectors came to Peter. The tax which they had to collect was the "Two-Drachma" Tax. (A Drachma is a Greek coin).

They collected the tax to pay for the Jewish Temple in Jerusalem. The Temple in those days was rather a costly place to run. The Jewish Church Services, and the Priests, and the High Priest expenses, all had to be paid for. In the Book of Exodus, the Law of Moses had laid down that a tax should be paid by every Jewish man.

The Tax Collectors asked Peter, "Does your Teacher pay the Temple Tax?" Peter answered, "Yes, he does." When Peter came into the house where they were staying, he was about to speak, but Jesus spoke first. Jesus said to Peter, "From whom do the Kings collect taxes and duties? Is it from their own sons, or is it from others?" Peter answered, "From others."

Jesus taught that we belong to two kingdoms. One which is an earthly kingdom which is the town or district where we live, and one is a heavenly kingdom. (The Church). Although we belong to the heavenly kingdom, (the Church), we should also pay for the upkeep of the earthly kingdom. (The local government). That is why even Christians must pay their rates and taxes.

Jesus then said, "So the King's sons are free from paying tax! However, in order that we may not offend the Tax Collectors, go to the Lake of Galilee, and throw out your fishing line. Open the mouth of the very first fish you catch, and inside it, you will find a four-drachma coin. Take it, and give it to the Tax Collectors to pay for your tax, and for mine. Peter went and did as he was told by Jesus. He caught a fish, and sure enough, there was a coin in the fish's mouth. He paid the Tax using the coin.

Of course, everyone will want to know how Jesus knew that there was a four - drachma coin in the fish's mouth. Children during the Second World War knew that there was money in lettuces, if they could grow them, and sell them to the shops. Rag-collectors knew that there was money in woollen rags, if they were collected, they could be sold.

If Jesus was telling Peter that if he caught fish and sold them, he could pay the tax then we could understand that meaning. However, if Peter actually found a coin inside the fish's mouth, then that explanation would make this story to be about a miracle. Many Christians believe that Jesus performed miracles.

Now why do you think that Jesus acted in this way? Probably, the Temple Tax-Collectors expected that Jesus would refuse to pay the Tax. They had laid a trap for Jesus. If he refused to pay the Tax, he would be reported to the authorities, and arrested. However, Jesus was wiser than his enemies. He agreed for the sake of keeping the Law that they should pay the tax after all.

From this story we learn that we are part of a society, to which everyone owes a duty. For instance, no-one has a legal right to watch television, except they have paid their television licence. Jesus meant that being born into a society brings its responsibilities.

Prayer:

> Heavenly Father, of the whole wide world,
> help us to realise that we owe duties
> to the society in which we live.
> Show us that we owe a duty to our family.
> Help us to be loyal to our school.
> Most of all, help us to be loyal to our Lord Jesus.   Amen.

Hymn:

> We are beating on the shore. (C&P.2. 84)
> or, Peace perfect peace, is the gift of Christ our lord. (C&P.1. 53)

Teachers' note: (1) Stories about Jesus are both very simple, and sometimes very difficult to understand. This story will be difficult for younger children. (2) Jesus taught that we owe duties to God, and to our society, and also to ourselves. *(Our* society could mean our community). (3) Jesus taught that we ought to keep the law of the land.

(b) The Mystery of Evil

Mysteries are sometimes very easy to understand. Stephen agreed to hammer down a few steps of his Grannies stair carpet. He felt very important, indeed, since he was using a hammer and tacks. His Grannie went into the kitchen to make him tea and scones. Stephen hammered in the first tack into the loose carpet. Then, his Grannie called through from the kitchen, asking him, whether he wanted sugar in his tea.

Then it happened. Stephen lost his hammer! He looked up the stairs, and down the stairs, but his hammer had vanished. He searched but nowhere could he see his hammer. Grannie came to look at how he was getting on with her carpet. Stephen called out, "Grannie I have lost my hammer!" Grannie laughed, and said, "You silly boy, how could you have lost the hammer, when it is in your hand?"

Sure enough, Stephen was holding the hammer, which he thought that he had lost. He felt rather silly, and not a little embarrassed. He had solved his mystery. Yet, he wondered about the first mystery of his forgetting that he had the hammer in his hand. Grannie, just said, "Stephen, many mysteries, are caused by ourselves. We become so deeply engrossed in what we are doing, that we live inside ourselves."

Some mysteries may even be funny. Just like the Vicar who used to lose his reading glasses. He looked all over the school-teacher's desk to find them. He would say, "This is a mystery, I had them five minutes ago." The children in the class used to smile, and call out, "Vicar, your glasses are on your head, above your eyebrows." So yet another mystery was solved.

Some mysteries are very serious and very sad. When children, who come from good homes, and who are well dressed, and who are well fed, commit acts of vandalism, then this is serious and very wrong. When children break window panes in old people's houses, we have the mystery of vandalism showing itself. When good teen-aged young people break into cars, these are mysteriously wicked acts. When a girl steals pencils from another girl in her own class, and proceeds to break them in pieces, then is part of the mystery of evil, which begins inside people.

The mystery of evil is explained by understanding that people often choose the evil inside them, rather than the good inside them. Jesus once told a story about a farmer who sowed wheat in his field. (Matt. 13: 30). When the wheat began to grow up as green shoots, the field also became full of thistle weeds. The Farmer knew that one of his enemies had sowed the thorns and thistles during the night.

His farm workers were going to root out all the thistles, but the farmer said, "Do not try to pull up these thorns and thistles, because you will also destroy the good growing-wheat as well. Let both grow together, until harvest-time. Then we will separate the wheat from the thorns and thistles. The weeds will be burned up.

The farmer had said, "An enemy has done this evil action." The mystery is why people choose evil in their minds, when they could as easily choose to do good. We need to understand that a "vandal" is an enemy of society. He or she is also an enemy to themselves.

Sow a thought, reap an act.
Sow an act, reap a habit.
Sow a habit, and reap a character.
Sow a character, and reap a destiny.

Criminals end up being put into prison, because they first of all, chose evil in their mind, rather than choosing good. Doing evil is a mystery. People say, "Why do they do it?" When we pray, it helps us to chose the good inside us, rather than the evil. We all have a choice.

Prayer:

Lord of all goodness, help us to choose
the good inside us, rather than the evil.
Help us to understand the mystery of evil.
Show us that doing good blesses the world.
Teach us that doing evil harms ourselves, and others.   Amen.

Hymn:

If I had a hammer. (C&P.1. 71)

Teachers' Note: (1) The issues here are clear enough. (2) God forgives us, and solves the mystery of guilt inside us. (3) Jesus is our perfect example.

(c) The Oil Mystery

Week 7   Mystery

There are some stories in the Bible that are difficult to explain. They are a mystery. Sometimes they can only be explained by thinking of them as parables. A parable is a story told with a deeper meaning in it.

Here is a mysterious story, which is found in Second Book of Kings, chapter four. The Teacher was named Elisha. There was also an adult school for Preachers, which was a gathering of men, who taught each other. One of the men who belonged to the Adult School had died. He left a widow, and two sons.

The widow woman came to tell Elisha that her husband had passed away. She said to Elisha, "My husband served the Lord, but at the time of his death, he owed another man a considerable sum of money. If I cannot repay this man my husband's debt, then the man will come and take my two sons away from me, and they will become his slaves. What shall I do?"

Elisha answered her, "What do you own at home? Do you not own anything which you could sell to pay the debt?" The woman replied, "The only thing I have is an earthen-ware jar with some oil in it." Elisha said, "Very good. Go and borrow from your friends and neighbours, all the jars and bottles you can get. Collect more than a few. Collect a lot of them."

The widow woman asked every person she knew, for the loan of bottles and jars. She and her two boys brought the jars and bottles inside her house. She began to pour the oil from her own jar into the jars which she had on loan. There were many jars. When she had filled one jar, she began to fill another. The two sons helped her. It seemed that the more oil she poured from her own jar, the more the oil just kept coming. She kept pouring, until she had filled all the jars and the bottles, except one. As she filled the last jar, her own jar went dry.

She took the oil in the containers to the merchant, and he bought up every jar of oil which she had for sale. The widow woman used the money which she had received for the oil, to pay off her husband's debt. Even then, she had enough money left to feed her two boys and herself for a long time.

This story may have a deeper meaning in it. The meaning could be that God always helps his people who are in need. Maybe, the meaning is that the more we give out, the more reserves we have in ourselves. Jesus once made a strange remark. He said ""Give and it shall be given unto you, pressed down, and running over." Maybe, the meaning is that Elisha was as powerful a Teacher as Elijah was before him. (Previously, Elijah had been very famous). The two Prophets, Elisha and Elijah' names are very similar. Remember, it was Elisha who is associated with this story.

Have you ever watched atheletes in practice. They know that the more they put into their exercises, the more they will get out of them. If we are learning, the more that we over-learn, the more that we will remember.

Prayer:

> Father God, we thank you
> for your care for each one of us.
> Help us to study more, that we may learn more,
> and be able to pour more knowledge out.
> Bless all widows and their families.   Amen.

Hymn:

Give me oil in my lamp. (C&P.1. 43), (JP. 50)

Teachers' Note: (1) We all agree that it is better not to get into too much debt. (2) This widow woman had a good friend in Elisha the Prophet. He gave her good advice. Her two sons helped their mother. (3) There are mysterious happenings in people's lives that may not always be immediately explained. God takes care of his people. Ref: 2. Kings Ch.4.

(a) The Flower Show

Week 8   Trying one's best

When Diane was nine years old she had her first sight of a field of Sun-flowers. It seemed to her that in the sunshine, the field was like a patchwork quilt of golden yellow. Diane had never seen flowers grow so high before. She went home to search her New Testament, because she remembered that somewhere in St. Matthew, that there was a verse about flowers. At last she found it. She read, "Jesus said, 'Consider how the flowers of the field grow. They do not labour or spin. Yet I tell you that even King Solomon in all his splendour was not dressed like one of these.'"

Her Village Flower Show Committee decided the following year, that they would give a special prize to the person who grew the tallest Sun-flower in the village. Diane was now ten years of age. She decided to enter the competition. She approached Farmer Fowler, to ask his advice. He smiled at Diane, and said, "If you go down to the end of our orchard, you will see several Sun-flowers growing just now. You may cut off one of the heads of any flower you like. Take it home and dry it out carefully, One flower will provide you with as many seeds, as you may need." Diane found the tall Sun-flowers. She cut off one flower head, put it into a paper bag and took it home.

She dried it out all that Winter in the boiler house. The flower head had hundreds of seeds in it. She only needed a few. Diane planted six Sun-flower seeds in six pots. All the seeds started to grow. They grew until they were about as high as Diane's knee. Then she dug holes in a sheltered place in the garden, beside a wall. She transplanted each flower, putting them into in the soil.

Diane knew that flowers needed to be watered, and fed, and protected from the wind. The six plants grew as tall as she was. She put rotting sea-weed into the soil around the plants. She strengthened the flowers by tying three Bamboo canes together, length-wise. The wind blew strongly some days, but the flowers did not blow down, because the thick bamboo canes held them up firmly. She carefully watered them every day. They grew much higher, until the month of August.

The Flower Show was held in the Village Hall. All sorts of flowers, and vegetables were being exhibited on long stalls. There was a special floor space, to show the Sun-flowers off to the public. On the Saturday morning, early, Diane dug up the tallest of her Sun-flowers. The Sun-flower now in a clay pot was huge, and very heavy. Farmer Fowler allowed Diane to ride on his tractor, while he carried Diane's Sun-flower on his trailer.

Farmer Fowler, carried the Sun-flower into the village Hall with great care. He paid the competition fee to the Officer at the door. The Officer gave him a ticket with a secret number on it. No names were allowed, so that the competition would be fairly carried out. The Officer also stuck the same ticket number underneath the pot. The Judging of the Sun-flowers was held during the afternoon.

When the time arrived, judging experts measured the large number of Sun-Flowers on show. Many people must have been secretly trying to grow the tallest Sun-flower. It was fortunate that the Village Hall had a very high ceiling. Farmer Fowler stood beside Diane. He gave the ticket to her. It was number 72. Diane held the ticket hidden in her hand. She was trembling with excitement. She wondered now, which Sun-flower belonged to her. There were so many, and they were all very tall. The Judges picked out one huge Sun-flower, and carried it into the middle of the floor. Every village gardener was hoping to win.

The Judge wearing the bowler hat, asked for silence. "Ladies and gentlemen, I declare that the Winner, for First Prize, is Number 72. If anyone here has got Number 72, please come forward." Diane read the number on her ticket again, just to be sure! Then, she stepped forward. Everyone gasped in surprise, and then they began to clap loudly.

The Judge said, "Bravo, Diane! You get the First Prize, a Gold Ribbon. The Special Gift this year is a hand-held computer game." Farmer Fowler, came forward, and congratulated Diane. Everyone clapped again. Diane could not believe her ears.

Afterwards, when she reached home on Farmer Fowler's tractor trailer, she rushed in to tell her Mum and Dad about her success at the competition. Later, Diane went upstairs, and opened her School Bible, and read the verse about flowers, again. "Jesus said, 'Consider how the flowers of the field grow. They do not labour or spin. Yet I tell you, that even King Solomon in all his splendour, was not dressed like one of these.' " (Matthew Chapter 6, verses 28-29.) She said a little prayer, "Thank you Lord, for helping me to grow the tallest Sun-flower in the village, and thank you for Farmer Fowler's encouragement. Amen."

This story shows that if even children really try, they can succeed. We may not always win prizes. Yet we can succeed in reaching our goals in life. Farmer

Fowler gave Diane a lot of encouragement. It is lovely to have genuine friends.
All successful adults were once children at school.

Prayer:

    Father God, we thank you for flowers.
    We thank you for gardeners.
    We thank you for the good soil,
    and the sunshine and the rain,
    which makes crops and flowers grow.   Amen.

Hymn:

    Have you heard the raindrops.drumming on the roof-tops.
    (C&P.1. 2) (JP. 71)

Teachers' Note: (1·) Diane knew that Farmer Fowler would help her. (2) Diane
took advice, and worked hard. She succeeded in growing a huge Sun-flower. The
hand-held computer game was an unexpected special reward; a bonus for her
attempt. Even if she had not won first prize, it would have all been worthwhile.
(3) Diane knew St. Matthew Chap. 6. verses 28-29.

(b) The Car Thief   *Week 8   Trying one's best*

Children sometimes hear adults say, "There but for the grace of God, go I."
Here is a story to explain what this means.

Kevin was an ordinary kind of boy. He happened to be passing a parked
car, when he noticed that the near side window had been left half open. Lying
on the back seat, was a cricket bat, and a cork ball. Kevin opened the car door
from the inside, making sure that no-one was looking. He stole the bat and the
cricket ball. He quickly carried them back to the garden hut behind his house.
This was Kevin's first crime. Now, he had become a criminal. He had made
himself into a car thief.

Kevin was a Scout, and he ought to have known better. When the Scouts went
away for a week-end camp, Kevin took the cricket bat, and the ball, with him to
the camp. Sadly, he had no stumps. The camp was held in a field where other
Scouts also were holding their week-end camp. The tents were erected very
quickly. The Scout-leaders decided to hold a cricket match. One of the
other Scout Troops were pleased to play as the opposing team. Unknown to
Kevin's troop, the Scout-leader of the opposing team was a Detective Policeman,
in his everyday work.

The Scouts used six short tent poles from another tent, as stumps. They
hammered in the three short poles at each end of the pitch. They used Kevin's big

bat and cork ball. They all had a turn at the wickets, and Kevin's team won the match. That evening at dusk, the three Scout Troops sat together in the darkness, around the camp fire, to sing songs, and to tell ghost stories. Later, the Scout-leader from the opposing team told the boys a story.

He said that there once was a Scout, who was a good, fair-minded boy. But for some strange reason, this good Scout, began to steal from parked cars. The Scout-leader said, that this boy even brought some of the goods which he stolen, to the Scout Camp, at the weekends. Without knowing, the other Scouts were using these stolen goods. It put them in a bad situation, in the eyes of the Local Police. It appeared that all the Scouts were thieves, which they were not.

The Scout-leader went on with his story, while the boys listened with interest. He said that the Scout-thief always felt guilty inside himself. Until one evening he asked God to forgive him. He then gathered into a large bag, everything which he had stolen over the short period. He left all the stolen articles on the desk of the Police Station, when no-one was looking.

That Scout became a changed person, and never stole anything again. "Would you believe it," the Scout-leader said, "that same Scout became a Policeman when he grew up. Stranger still, that person was trusted enough by his Troop, to be allowed to become a Scout-leader. And no-one ever knew about his past criminal actions; only God knew. He made up his mind, never again to lose the respect of his Scout Troop. Now boys, that is the end of my true story."

The boys had enjoyed the story, but Kevin felt very uneasy. He realised that the Scout-leader had recognised the stolen cricket bat and ball, while they were playing the match. Yet, he had been silent, and had not even looked at Kevin, nor had he accused anyone. Kevin knew that the Policeman-Scout-leader was making a silent appeal to Kevin himself, to stop stealing, and to restore what he had stolen. The following day, the Scouts returned home from camp.

Strange to say, that very next evening, in the darkness someone had come up to the Local Police station, and he had left a cricket bat and a cork ball in a parcel on the Police desk inside. No note was left, nor was any name on the parcel. The Police Sergeant recognised the bat and ball, as those listed as stolen from a car some weeks before.

He thought to himself. Some boy has stolen this bat and ball, and then later thought it better to return the goods. Motorists should not be careless, and leave their car windows open. They cause people to steal. People also should have enough honesty that they could pass an open car window without stealing. Both are to blame. Anyway, all is well that ends well! The Desk Sergeant returned the bat and ball to the car owner.

Prayer:

> Heavenly Father, teach us at all times to be honest.
> We thank you for every boy or girl
> who repents of wrong-doing.
> We thank you, that our God is willing
> to forgive us our sins, if we confess them to him.   Amen.

Hymn:

> Peace perfect peace, is the gift of Christ our Lord. (C&P.1. 53)

Teachers' Note: (1) Kevin was a thief. (2) Kevin had been found out. Yet the Policeman-Scout Leader also had once been a little boy, and he had himself once stolen goods. He had restored the goods, and had been helped by God to change his character. (We know this because the Policeman told the story about himself). (3) Maybe, Kevin also later became a Policeman. It is possible! "Thou shalt not steal," is the emphasis here.

(c) **Mary and Martha**   *Week 8   Trying one's best*

Jesus sometimes was kept so busy, that he became very tired, and he had to take a day or two of rest. This was much like the way that everyone needs a little holiday, now and again. He knew that he could always visit the home of Mary and Martha in the village of Bethany.

On one of these occasions when Jesus needed a rest, he visited the house at Bethany. He knew that he could always have peace and quietness there. The two ladies would provide him with three good meals a day. After his journeys, he would have a clean bed to rest himself upon, when he needed to rest. When Jesus arrived at the house, Mary and Martha made him very welcome. They invited him inside.

Martha loved to serve her visitors. She was a mass of energy. When Jesus arrived she was no different. She worked and fussed about having everything perfect for the first meal. She went around dusting all the furniture. She put out a white clean table-cloth. She cooked the meal. She put out all the cups and plates. She arranged the chairs around the table. While all this work was going on, her sister Mary, just sat by the fireside, and talked with Jesus. She listened to what Jesus had to tell her, and Jesus listened to Mary's news.

Martha suddenly realised that she was doing all the work, and that her sister, Mary was just sitting and talking. Martha complained to Jesus. "Lord, speak to Mary, so that she comes to help me with all the work of preparing this meal. Tell her to help me!" she said.

Jesus replied, "Martha, you have really been very busy, and that is a good thing to do. However, on this occasion, Mary has just had a conversation with me. She has chosen to do the better part of entertaining her guest. Just now I needed friendship, and peace. Mary has provided both. I shall not take away from her, the better part of welcoming a guest."

Of course, Jesus appreciated the splendid manner in which Martha was preparing the delicious meal for him. Martha was really a good cook. Mary had a more gentle nature, and she realised that what Jesus needed most of all, was some friendship. Mary realised that Jesus was weary and tired at that moment. Very soon they all sat around the table, and they all had an enjoyable meal. After which Jesus had a good night's rest. He woke up refreshed next morning.

The reason Mary's part was the better part was because Mary offered the right kindness at the correct time to Jesus. We must learn to judge the proper time to do a kindness to anyone. There is a time for talking, and a time for working, and a time for relaxing. We must always try to understand the importance of the moment. Do you know when you should keep quiet? Do you know when you should be working as hard as you can? Do you know when you are free to do as you please? Do you know when you can share a secret, and when you must keep matters to yourself?

Prayer:

Heavenly Father, God of love,
We thank you for such people, as Martha and Mary.
who opened up their home to Jesus.
We thank you for Martha's hard work in the home.
We also thank you for Mary's quiet friendship.
Teach us to be faithful followers of Jesus.   Amen.

Hymn:

Come and praise the Lord, our King. (C&P.1. 21). (JP. 34)

Teachers' Note: (1) Martha was an excellent worker, but inclined to be a little fussy. (2) Mary offered Jesus what he needed most at that particular time, which was a quiet conversation. (3) Both women had good points. They both opened up their home to Jesus. He always left their home, well refreshed afterwards. How do you treat visitors to your home?

(a) Abraham the Father   *Week 9   The Jews*

Abraham was really the Father of the Jewish people. When the people of the Jewish religion are speaking of their God, they often call him, "The God of

Abraham, Isaac, and Jacob." Now Isaac was Abraham's son, and Jacob was Abraham's grandson. So, you can see, just how important Abraham is for the history of the Jewish people. All Jewish events date back to Abraham.

It all began when God spoke to Abraham. God said to him, "Abraham, I am going to make a covenant (agreement) with you. You will become the father of many people. If you keep my covenant and do what is right, then I will give to you this land of Canaan, in which you are now a stranger. More than all that, I will give this land to your children, and their descendents."

God said to Abraham, "You are no longer to call your wife "Sarai" but rather call her "Sarah". She will give birth to a son." When Abraham heard God say that he would have a son, Abraham fell down on his face, and laughed. He said to himself, "How can a man who is one hundred years old, and whose wife is ninety years old, have a baby in the family. We are too old."

Some time afterwards, Abraham saw three strange men near his tent. Abraham was a nomad, and he was always travelling about with his flocks. Eastern nomad people are very hospitable to visitors. Abraham invited his visitors into his tent to share their food. Sarah made the three visitors a very tasty meal.

Before the meal, they brought water in a basin to wash their visitors' feet. This was the custom in that part of the country. It was a sign of welcome. The three visitors were sent from God to confirm the good news that Abraham's wife, Sarah, would bear a son the very next year.

When it actually happened, and the little boy was born, as the three men had foretold, they called the new baby, "Isaac". So it happened, that although Abraham was one hundred years old, and Sarah was ninety years old, their home was blessed with a baby boy. Abraham and Isaac were ever so happy.

The age of Abraham and Sarah will make us wonder. People generally do not live to such an age nowadays. Telling one's age means that we are using a particular calendar. We know that ancient people used the moon to measure out their time. (New moon, first half moon, full moon, and the last quarter). It would be easier to understand Abraham's age, if there were less moons in an ancient year than the number of moons which we have in our calendar year. (Less moons would result in a higher age). The later Jewish Calendar is also fixed by phases of the moon.

Prayer:

> Heavenly Father, we thank you for the faith of Abraham.
> We thank you that Abraham and Sarah in their old age,
> were able to have their baby after all.
> We pray for all Jewish people everywhere,
> especially in the city of Jerusalem.   Amen.

Hymn:

    I want to see your baby boy. (C&P.2. 117)

Teachers' Note: (1) Abraham and his wife Sarah were both good people who loved the Lord. (2) They were really too old to have a baby in their family. Yet, God was good to them, and Isaac was born. (3). Abraham although a man of strong faith in God, sometimes like all human beings, had his own private doubts. Reference Genesis Chapter 18.

(b) Praying for Others

The time came for Abraham's three visitors to leave. The strangers went on their way. They walked as if they were going towards the two wicked cities, Sodom and Gomorrah.

The wrong-doing of these two cities was so terrible, that God was angry with them. Now, God told Abraham his intentions. He said that he was about to destroy the two evil cities, Sodom and Gomorrah. Abraham was a good man, and he had a kind heart. Abraham prayed and pleaded with God, that if there were fifty good people in the cities, that he would spare them. God agreed to spare the towns from destruction, if fifty good people could be found there. Sad to say, there were not fifty good living people in Sodom and Gomorrah.

Abraham prayed to God again, "Lord, if there are forty-five good people in the two towns, will you spare them?" Yet, they could not find forty-five good people. Abraham prayed once more, that if they could find forty good people, that God would spare the two cities. Even forty good people could not be found. Abraham once again prayed to God, "Lord, will you spare these towns if you can find thirty good people?" Yet, there was not even thirty good people to be found in Sodom and Gomorrah.

Abraham did not give up pleading for the people of Sodom and Gomorrah. "Lord, if I can find twenty good people, will you spare the cities." God said, "Yes." Yet, they could not find even twenty good people there. As a last attempt, Abraham, pleaded with God, "Lord If I can find ten good people, will you spare these cities." God agreed, once more. Yet, there were not even ten good people to be found in Sodom and Gomorrah.

Very soon there was a volcanic eruption in a mountain nearby, and the black burning sulphur ashes began to fall like firey rain, on Sodom and Gomorrah. Soon, the cities were set ablaze and all the buildings were destroyed. The destruction had actually happened.

Abraham and his family took up their tents and moved on to new pastures, with their flocks of sheep and goats. The wonderful thing was that God felt that he could trust Abraham.

Nowadays, Jews everywhere, look to Israel as their native country, because God promised the land to Abraham, and to his children's children, so long ago. Here is God's promise to Abraham. "I will give to you and to your children after you, the land wherein you are now a stranger, all the land of Canaan, for an everlasting possession. I will be their God." Genesis Ch. 17, vers 10.

Prayer:

    Lord God, of Abraham, Isaac, and Jacob,
    We give you thanks for Abraham's faithfulness.
    We thank you that our Lord Jesus Christ,
    was born into a Jewish home.
    We pray for all Jewish children all over the world.
    Bless our school and our Teachers.   Amen.

Hymn:

    Make me a channel of your peace. (C&P.2. 147), (JP. 161)

Teachers' Note: (1) Abraham prayed for other people. (2) There will always be wicked people in the world. (3) We must not conclude that every volcano explosion, today is caused by evil people. These are natural events. Reference, Genesis Chapter 18 and 19.

(c) Isaiah's Call   *Week 9   The Jews*

Isaiah was a Jew who lived in the days of King Uzziah. The King was his friend. In the same year which King Uzziah died, something happened which changed Isaiah's outlook in life. Isaiah had a remarkable vision. A vision is more like a day-dream, than anything else. The effect of a vision may change the course of one's whole life.

In the vision, Isaiah saw the Lord, seated on a great throne in the Jewish Temple. The Lord's robe was so large and long, that it was like a bride's wedding train. It filled the whole of the Temple. Just above the throne, there were winged beings, like angels. These angelic beings were called "Seraphs."

Each Seraph had six wings. The Seraphs covered their faces with two wings. They covered their feet with another two wings. With yet another two wings they were flying. Isaiah was mystified, as to what these six-winged angelic beings were doing. The Seraphs were calling one to another, "Holy, Holy, Holy, is the Lord Almighty; the whole earth is full of God's glory".

In the vision, the noise was so great, that the door-posts of the Temple began to shake. The Temple building was filled with smoke. Isaiah was so frightened that he called out, "Pity me. I am ruined! For I am a man of unclean lips, and I live among a people who have unclean lips. For my eyes have seen the King, the Lord almighty."

Then one of the Angelic Seraphs flew to Isaiah. The Seraph held a red hot piece of burning coal, which he had taken with the tongs from off the Temple altar fire. The Seraph touched Isaiah's lips with the red hot flaming coal, and Isaiah was not burned. The Seraph said, "Look, this has touched your lips, Isaiah, and your sin is taken away."

At that moment, Isaiah heard a voice of the Lord calling. The voice said, "Who shall I send? Who will go for us? "Isaiah realised that God was calling him. So, he answered, "Here am I Lord. Send me!" The Lord answered Isaiah, by saying, "Isaiah, go and tell my people the good news." From that day forward, Isaiah became the Lord's messenger. He preached God's truth to the people.

How do we receive published news today? We could receive it by letter, or by radio, or by television, or by video, or by newspaper. Many years ago, most big towns paid for a Town Crier, who went about ringing a bell each hour of the day when he announced the latest news.

He would call out at the top of his voice, "Oyez, Oyez! It is six o'clock. There was a fire in the tailor's shop on High Street last night. All is well! The Vicar has a bad cold, and the Reverend Mr.Green will be taking the morning service this Sunday morning. All is well! Mrs. Smith has had a baby girl, at half past three this afternoon, and both mother and child are doing fine. All is well! The King will open Parliament next Tuesday. All is well! Children should be in their beds at eight o'clock these dark evenings. All is well! Dr. Dunn will be in town on Thursday morning, patients take notice and attend early. All is well! Oyez. Oyez!" Then he would ring his bell again, and move on to another street to give the News.

Isaiah became God's messenger. He was a little like a Town Crier. He would gather the people together, and announce "Thus says the Lord God. "You must change your bad habits. You must keep the Lord God's commandments. You must not rob the poor. You must pay your workers fair wages for their work. The Lord God, says, if you obey me all will be well. If you do not obey the call to good behaviour, then the Lord will be angry with you. Hear the Word of the Lord!"

What announcements given at school, can you remember right now?

Prayer:

Good Lord, we thank you for Isaiah's call.
We thank you for every person who has

answered the call to serve other people.
We pray for Doctors and Nurses,
for Teachers and Ministers, (or Priests),
for Judges and Lawyers,
that they all may do what is right in God's sight.   Amen.

Hymn:

Colours of the day, dawn into the mind. (C&P.1. 55), (JP. 28)

Teachers' Note: A bell used at the proper place with this assembly can make it very effective. (1) The remarkable feature here is that Isaiah had a vision of the Lord sitting on a throne. The Hebrew faith teaches that God is unseen and invisible. (2) Notice that even the angelic beings called Seraphs worshipped God. (3) The most important fact, in the vision, was that Isaiah obeyed the call of the Lord. He became God's Messenger. Children's ambitions with God's help, may turn into visions of success. Reference Isaiah Chapter 6.

(a) Second Sight   *Week 10   Second Things*

Grandad was eighty years of age. He had a car, which he loved to drive. Grandad always thought that he was a very good driver. One morning the Postman brought him a letter, which said that he had to under-go an eyesight test, before he could get another licence to drive his car. Off he went to meet the Optician. Both Grandad and the Optician sat inside his car.

Grandad was asked to read the Registration number of the car, parked before him. He read out, "N 337 HGV. The Tester, said, to Grandad, "I am sorry Mr. Mackay, but you have read this number incorrectly. It should read as "R 887 ECV. I am sorry to tell you that your eyes are becoming weaker. You will need to wear glasses all the time. I shall Test you once more, in one month's time, and if you fail the Reading Test next time, then you will not be allowed to drive a car, ever again.

Grandad went home, very perplexed. He went to an Optician's Shop on the main street. He asked for a new pair of glasses. In order to be sure of getting the right glasses, he had to read printed letters, printed on a card, hanging on the wall. The printed letters became smaller, and smaller. Some letters were red, and some were green. Grandad was asked to point out, the colour of the letters. Grandad did very well in this test. In one week's time, Grandad received his new glasses, from the Optician's shop.

Now he could read all the numbers on other cars. He could see the colour of the traffic lights very clearly; Green, Amber, and Red. Grandad was very relieved when the Optician tested him a second time, and Grandad passed the test on this occasion, even though it was the second time. He was allowed to drive a car for another three years.

There is a story in the New Testament very like this story. There was a blind man, whom the people brought to be healed. Jesus stretched out his hand, and he touched the blind man's eyes. "What can you see?" asked Jesus. The man said, "I can see people, as if they were trees walking." Jesus knew immediately, that the man could see a little, but not clearly enough. So he dampened his finger, and anointed the Blind man's eyes, and then he touched them a second time. After the second touch by Jesus, the blind man could see clearly. He had been cured. He became a very happy man, that day.

Prayer:

> Heavenly Father,
> we know that there are some things in life,
> Which need a second effort.
> Help us if we fail the first time,
> that we shall try, and try again.
> We pray for all blind people, that Doctors
> may bring about healing and relief.   Amen.

Hymn:

> He gave me eyes so I could see. (C&P.1. 18)
> or, Amazing Grace, how sweet the sound. (JP. 8)

Teachers' Note: (1) Grandad needed a second test to see whether he could see correctly. When Jesus healed the blind man, the man needed a second touch, to see clearly. (3) Many of our first attempts are very poor, indeed. Often a second attempt, puts matters right. A re-sit at an examination, often helps us. Reference Mark Ch. 8. verses 22-26.

(b) Second Wind

Week 10   Second Things

An old Yorkshire seaman tells this story. "On the coast of North Yorkshire, there are two beautiful seaside villages. One is named, "Runswick Bay", and one is named "Staithes." Long ago they had a Life-boat at Staithes, which really was only a wooden rowing-boat. The brave lifeboatmen would put on their oilskin clothes, and launch their little life-boat down the ramp at Staithes, and row out into the stormy North sea, to rescue people on board a wrecked ship. The Lifeboatmen were never afraid of the sea, but they all had a great respect for it. They were never careless when sailing on the sea.

Runswick Bay is about three miles away by road, from Staithes village. One stormy day there was a sailing boat in distress, off the shore at Runswick Bay. There was a bright boy, at Runswick bay, who hoped that he might become a Lifeboatman, when he grew up, but he was still only a boy. His name was Tom. One of the Runswick Bay fishermen came running along the rocky path, shouting "We need the Staithes Life-boat. There is a sailing ship in the bay, being washed against the rocks."

Tom heard the fishermen's call for help. Tom shouted in the wind, "I shall run across the fields and over the cliff path, to tell the Staithes Lifeboatmen, to put out the lifeboat." Tom ran up the hill, and across the field, and around the high cliff towards Staithes village. He had run nearly half-of the distance, when he felt that he could run no more. He was tired and exhausted all over his body.

Tom remembered one of the Bible verses that he had heard in the little Runswick Bay Methodist Chapel. "They who wait upon the Lord, shall renew their strength. They shall mount up with wings as eagles, they shall run, and not be weary, they shall walk and not faint." The sky was dark, and the wind was strong, and the rain was pouring down. Tom prayed for strength.

Tom remembered that he was told at school, that when animals begin to run, that they become very hot, but that after a short time running, their bodies atune to the running, in a natural manner. The animals get "second wind" which makes them run faster than ever. Tom prayed, as he ran, "Lord, give me a second wind" Just at that moment, the pain in Tom's chest ceased, and he knew that he could run for miles if he had to. He kept running across the cliffs until he reached the place, where he could run down the hill, and into Staithes Village.

Tom ran down the main street in Staithes, shouting "They need the Life-boat in Runswick Bay. There is a ship on the rocks". There were no telephones in those days. The wife of the Coxswain of the lifeboat, wearing her quaint little Staithes bonnet, heard Tom's message. She ran to call out the Lifeboat crew. These brave men, tried to launch the Lifeboat, but the waves were so high, that they could not get the lifeboat into the sea.

Then one of them had a strange idea. They decided to carry their lifeboat up to the top of the grassy cliff top at Staithes, and then to carry it further across the fields, all the way to Runswick bay, on this terribly stormy day. Tom helped the crew members carry the lifeboat over the hedges, and across two miles of fields, until they reached Runswick Bay. Then they launched the lifeboat, in a raging storm. The waves were large and very rough. The storm blew the spray all over the fishing people's houses.

Tom, watched the boat powered only by oarsmen, go out over the raging sea. In a few hours, the lifeboat came back, carrying the men, women, and children from the sinking ship. Everyone on the shore cheered. They helped the freezing, hungry, soaking-wet people into the fishermen's houses, where they warmed up and received hot meals.

The Fishermen went back to Staithes. The boy, Tom, from Runswick Bay, closed his eyes, and thanked God that he had found his second wind that stormy day. He had been enabled to carry the call for help. The brave Staithes people, had volunteered to save the sinking ship. Everyone sometimes needs a second wind.

The old Yorkshire Seaman who told this story, said, "It is strange that everyone knows about the storm, and the brave Staithes Lifeboat men, but no-one remembers about Tom, the fisherman's son".

(The Bible verse which Tom remembered is, "They who wait upon the Lord, shall renew their strength. They shall mount up with wings as eagles. They shall run and not be weary. They shall walk and not faint." Isaiah Chapter 40, verses 31.)

Prayer:

> Father in Heaven, give us all a second-wind,
> in the race through this life,
> that we may pursue that which is pure and good.
> We pray for all sailors, as they sail
> the high seas, and stormy waves.
> We pray for lifeboatmen, and their families.　　Amen.

Hymn:

> In the morning early, I go down to the sea. (C&P.1. 60)

Teachers' Note: (1) Tom was a brave boy, carrying an urgent message. His prayer for strength, came as a second wind, in his race against the storm. (2) Sometimes we grow tired in performing good deeds. We all like runners, need a second wind, to finish the race. (3) Isaiah Chapter 40 verse 31, helped Tom to continue. The Holy scriptures are always helpful.

(c) Second-Hand Books

John loved looking at second hand books. (Anything which is said to be "second hand" has been owned by someone else, and later sold and bought a second time). The second-hand article might be a week old, or it might be one hundred years of age. Probably, the person who owned an old book, might have died a long time ago, and the contents of their house were sold by an auctioneer. That is perhaps, how some second hand books ended up in a bookshop. Many of the old books had been school prizes which had been awarded to children many years ago.

John, knew quite a lot about books. He liked to read new children's books, and he also borrowed books from the local library, and out of the school library. He knew that most second hand books were cheaper than new books. He knew that opening up a second-hand book is a bit of an adventure, because you may find something very old between the pages. However, most of all, John liked the second-hand book shops.

His Teacher had introduced John to the Bible. John found that the Bible was not just one book, but that it was a little library on it's own. In the Old Testament, there were thirty-nine books. In the New Testament, there were twenty seven books. Added together, that made sixty-six books in his own Bible. (Jesus used to like reading the Prophet Isaiah). John could rhyme off by heart, the names of all the sixty-six books, just as if he were saying A. B. C. D.

It was Saturday morning, when John was off school. He wandered down the main street, to visit the second-hand book shop. There were many dusty books for sale. John bought two books that day. He bought "Charlie and the Chocolate Factory" by Roald Dahl, and "Sophie's Tom" by Dick King Smith. Both books cost ten pence each. John thought to himself, if I do not waste my pocket money, then I can come down here every Saturday morning, and buy one book at least.

Then at the end of the year, I would have my own library at home. So John continued to buy one book, every week. His Dad built him a bookcase from beautiful new wood which he had in the garage. John varnished it. Now, in his bedroom, he had his library. He counted nearly one hundred books in his bookcase.

At school, the Teacher, noticed that John was reading faster than anyone in the class. His written work, had improved more than anyone else. He could write stories, and really good descriptions of almost anything, because he was reading so many other books. John was learning fast. When a good book was being serialised on the television, then John watched the television, and read the book afterwards. Soon, his Dad had to make him a second bookcase, as his books increased in number. Although, his Mum did not like to have to dust the second hand books, she did it for John's sake.

One day, John read that schools in parts of Africa were bi-lingual. That meant that they learnt subjects in their own language, and they also learnt English. They had very few books to read in English. The Mission Schools (schools run by the Churches) sent out an appeal to people in England, asking them to send books of all kinds, packed inside strong wooden boxes, for the use of the African boys and girls. The African school children learnt the English language much faster, if they read a story in English.

John, loved his books more than his toys but when he heard the appeal, he thought to himself, "If I gave away all my books to the African School children, then I suppose that I could start collecting books all over again." So John and his Dad bought seven tea-chests, which were large ply-wood boxes. They packed the books into the boxes, and addressed them to the Mission School in West Africa.

The African Children were delighted, to receive the story books that John had sent out by ship. They sent back a letter, thanking John, and signed by fifty African children. John felt that he had genuinely helped children of the third world. He looked at the empty shelves in his two book-cases. He thought to himself, "I shall start another library."

Next Saturday morning, John was shopping on the main street. Can you guess which shop, John visited first? (Yes! It was the second-hand book-shop.) However, when he went in, he got a big surprise. The owner of the shop had heard what John had done for the African children, so he gave John a Gift Book Token.

This Token is like a folded card with a value stamp inside it, (£5 or £10), which the customer may exchange for any book they want to buy, to the value of the Token. John felt that the sacrifice of his beloved books had been rewarded. He used the Gift Book-Token to buy two brand new books this time. They were the first books in his second library.

Prayer:
> Heavenly Father, teach us that it is more blessed
> to give than to receive.
> Help us all in our search for knowledge.
> Show us as children, how to read, understand,
> and inwardly digest, what we read.
> Bless the school children of Africa.   Amen.

Hymn:
> Thank you, Lord for this new day. (C&P.1. 32), (JP. 232)

Teacher's Note: (1) John loved books of all kinds. We begin with picture books, and then go on to easy reading books, before attempting to read larger books. (2) Books are a source of knowledge. The Bible is a good book to read, but often difficult to understand. Saint Mark's Gospel is a good interesting book to begin the reading of the Bible, or Saint John's Gospel from Chapter two. (3) Reading helps us to write and understand other subjects. (Jesus read Isaiah. See St. Luke Chapter 4. verse 18 and 19).

(a) **For the Want of a Nail**

Do you think that small things matter? There was once a king who had a messenger. The King entrusted all his secret messages to this horseman, because he had such a fine fast travelling horse. The messenger put the King's written message into a special wallet, attached to his leather belt, inside his coat. Then he would ride his horse, and speed like the wind over hill, forest and dale. He would not rest for long, until he had delivered the king's message to the receiver.

One day, the King entrusted him with a special message, which was to be delivered to a King in another country. He was warning his fellow King that an enemy was preparing a war against him. His secret message was to ensure that the other King would be ready for war, should it happen. As the messenger was riding his horse, he noticed that his horse was limping slightly. He dismounted, and examined the horse's foot. One of the nails which held the horse-shoe on had become very loose.

The King's messenger, had become careless about his horse's welfare. He thought to himself, that he need not bother about such a small thing as a horse-shoe nail falling out. So he continued to ride the horse, as fast as he could, when he ought to have gone to the village blacksmith, and had a new nail, hammered into his horse's iron shoe.

After a day, the iron horseshoe became even more loose, and after another half-day the horse shoe fell off. A horse which runs wearing only three shoes, soon suffers from sore feet. After a time, it cannot run very fast, and eventually the horse will slow up, and then come to a halt. This is exactly what happened to the messenger's horse.

The messenger was left in the middle of a lonely road, with a lame horse. He failed to deliver the King's secret message on time, to his neighbour King. The enemy came with his army, and surprised the neighbouring King. There was a fierce battle, and because he had been surprised by his enemy's army, he lost the battle. His enemy having won the battle, won the remainder of the war, and the enemy ruler conquered the whole kingdom.

If the messenger had been more careful, and taken care of his horses hooves, the horse would not have become lame. The secret message would have arrived on time. The neighbouring King having been warned, would have been ready for his enemy. Everything in the war had been lost, because of a horse-shoe nail. Small things are very important. You would not like to have a thorn sticking into the under-sole of your foot. The person who is careful in small, things, will also be successful with large things.

Sailors often say, that a ship can be lost, for the sake of a pennyworth of tar. Do you understand what it means? There is a verse in the Book of Proverbs which says, "See a man who is diligent in his business, he shall stand before kings." Reference. Proverbs 22v23. Diligence is being careful about small things. Do you always put a full stop at the end of your sentence, when you write?

Children may know the rhyme. It reads like this:

For the want of a nail, the shoe was lost.
For the want of a shoe, the horse was lost.
For the want of a horse, the rider was lost.
For the want of a rider, the message was lost.
For the want of a message, the battle was lost.
For the want of a battle, the Kingdom was lost.
All for the want of a horse-shoe nail.

Prayer:

Heavenly Father teach us to be faithful
in small things, as Jesus was.
Give us patience to complete our tasks.
May we not be half-hearted or careless
at school or at home.
Help us to value small kindnesses shown to us.   Amen.

Hymn:

Carpenter, carpenter, make me a tree. (C&P.1. 5),
or, The earth is yours. (C&P.1. 6)

Teachers' Note: (1) Small things are very important in life. (2) Being careless about small things leads to large mistakes. (3) Jesus loved small children and he had time for them.

(b) Lost Needle in a Hay-Barn   *Week 11   Small Things*

Mrs. Grower the farmer's wife, made beautiful patchwork quilts for the bed. People who liked Victorian style bedrooms, would order a new patchwork quilt. Mrs. Grower never used a sewing machine. Instead, she had a sixteenth century large curved needle, which was similar to the needle which a Doctor may use, to sew up a wound. She showed it to everyone who called at her farmhouse. She said that her ancestor-grandparents, who had lived far into the past, had sewed bed-clothes for King Henry the Eighth. That was the story which she told to new customers, who wanted her to make a new patchwork quilt for them.

Tracy, her grand-daughter came to visit her grand-mother, Mrs. Grower. She had brought her rag doll with her. Patch, the farm dog had run away with the rag doll in his teeth. Tracy, had pulled the rag doll out of Patch's mouth, and the rag doll had become torn. Tracy did not want to make a fuss, so she took her

Grand-mother's ancient sewing basket out to the barn. She sewed the rag-doll up again, using her grand-mother's famous curved King Henry the Eighth sewing needle.

Then, the disaster happened. Tracy was sure that she had the sewing needle on her lap, but when she stood up, to shut the great iron sliding door of the barn, she found that she had lost Grandmother's famous needle. It really was a needle lost in a haystack. There were many haystacks of hay packed high in the hay-barn. What could she do? She dare not tell her Grand-mother.

Tracy ran to tell her friend, Tony Nugent. He was a bright boy, and loved learning about mechanical things. Tony went in to the barn with Tracy, but the hay was all over the barn floor. Neither of them could find the precious sixteenth century curved sewing needle.

Tony Nugent sat down to think. Then he said, "I have a magnet at our house. If I tied the horse-shoe shaped magnet to a string, then we could trail it over the hay. The needle must be somewhere near where you were sitting in the barn. Imagine trying to find a needle in a hay shed."

So, Tony Nugent came back to the hay-barn with his horse-shoe shaped magnet. He tied it to a string, and dragged it behind him, as he walked about the barn. He walked about for half an hour, but they could not find the precious ancient needle. They both went home for tea, and they the agreed to look again They dared not tell Grand-mother, because that needle had been in the family possession for hundreds of years.

After tea, the two children, took turns at dragging the magnet over the hay barn floor. Tony Nugent was becoming a little tired walking up and down the hay-barn, so Tracy took another turn. She searched up and down, and down and up, across the hay. She lifted her coat out of the way, and as she shook the hay off it, something shiny seemed to jump and stick on to the magnet. It, sure enough, was the curved iron sewing needle from the sixteenth century. The magnet had attracted the needle. The precious lost needle was found.

Tracy put the needle back into Grand-mother's pin cushion. She put the pin cushion, into the sewing basket. Then she returned the basket to Grand-mother's sitting room. Tracy and Tony Nugent, never told anyone about their adventure. However, when anyone had lost something, and they said, "It was like looking for a needle in a haystack," Tracy and Tony Nugent always looked at each other and smiled. They knew the feeling too. Small things can be such a nuisance, when they are lost. Patch the dog seemed to understand, what the smiles meant.

Small things are very important in life. It is lovely to hear young people saying, "Thank You" to someone. It is only a small thing to do, but how lovely are good manners. Jesus said, "Suffer the little children to come unto me. For of such is the kingdom of Heaven." Jesus really loved small children.

Small people are important to God. There were once little brass monkey ornaments, which sat on peoples' mantlepieces, especially in farm houses. There were three monkeys sitting in a row. One held its hands over its eyes: One held it's hands over it's ears: One held its hands over its mouth. The monkey ornament meant, "See no evil. Hear no evil. Speak no evil." These were small signs in the home, but everyone knew what they meant.

Prayer:

> Help us Lord to be careful in small matters.
> Help us to avoid even small unkind acts.
> May we may do small kindnesses to others.
> Make us faithful in small things.
> Bless all sick children in our own country.
> We pray for the children of the third world.   Amen.

Hymn:

> Think of all the things we lose. (C&P.1. 57)

Teachers' Note: (1) Tracy had lost her Grand-mother's precious curved needle. (2) It is the most difficult thing to find a needle in a hay-shed. Tony Nugent must have known something about magnetics. It was fortunate that he owned a horse-shoe shaped magnet. There are many important things in life which are small matters. Saying, "Thank you," washing one's hand before meals, bringing a handkerchief to school every day, saying your prayers at night, practising good manners, or going an errand for your parent. Can you think of other important small things in life?

(c) **Little Accidents**   *Week 11   Small Things*

Accidents can happen anywhere. We must always be careful, if we are to avoid little accidents happening to us. King William, the Third, was a Dutchman who came over from Holland, with his Queen, who was named Mary. William became King of England. He fought the forces of King James the second, who had fled to Ireland. William's army won the battles of 1690. King James fled the country and there was peace again.

King William loved to ride his horse. He was an expert horseman. (William had one serious fault, he is reported to have been very greedy at the meal table, as he really liked his food). Then, one day he had his accident.

Underneath the grass at Hampton Court, there lived little velvet coated moles. These little animals burrowed long tunnels under the ground. Every now and again, the moles would come up to the top of the ground. When they had come up to the fresh air, they always left a mole-hill on the top of the ground. They would disappear underground again to make more tunnels.

King William was riding his horse in the grounds of Hampton Court. His horse is usually shown in paintings as a white horse. His horse was galloping across the grass, when it suddenly stumbled over the soft ground, and it fell over a mole hill, which it did not see, until it was too late to avoid it. King William was thrown off his horse to the ground. He probably had broken his collar bone. His servants carried him home to the palace. He lay in bed, seriously ill. As a result of his fall, he died early in the year 1702.

In the later reign of Queen Anne his successor, the Jacobites, who were supporters of the defeated King James, used to drink a toast, holding up their wine-glasses. They would say, "Here is to the little Gentleman in velvet." They meant that the mighty King of England had been killed accidentally by a little velvet-coated mole. This event in history teaches us, that accidents may happen to anyone, even though it be a King!

Accidents may be caused by carelessness. Harry was told by his Dad that he was not to ride his new bike across the Zebra Crossing. He was told that he could push the bike across. His teacher also warned him about the danger of riding too fast along the footpath, and perhaps, knocking some old lady down. One day on the way from school, Harry was pedalling furiously along the footpath, when he did not wait on the Lollipop lady stopping the traffic. Harry peddled his bike off the pavement He thought to himself, "I am safe on the black and white crossing."

The trouble was that the motorist did not see Harry pedalling very fast off the pavement across the road. Instead of the motorist hitting Harry, it was Harry who hit the side of motorist's car, when he was on the Zebra crossing. This might have been a serious accident, but for the fact that the car had very good brakes. The car stopped instantly. Harry's new bike was a wreck, and Harry had to be taken to hospital in the ambulance, with many cuts and bruises. So, careless people sometimes cause accidents.

An accident may be a genuine mistake. Such a mistake was made by Alister, when he first played football for his school team. Alister made up his mind to score a goal, in his first football match. So, he ran here, there, and everywhere, across the football field. He became so hot that the sweat was pouring down his forehead. Alister was running very fast, when he saw a goal mouth appear before his eyes. He took good aim, and he kicked with his left foot, because he was left handed. He scored a beautiful goal. Everyone on Alister's side groaned, because Alister had scored a goal through his own goal-posts. He had kicked the ball in the wrong direction. It was a genuine mistake on Alister's part.

Sometimes we narrowly escape accidents by double-checking what we are doing. Jenny was helping her Mum to give a bath to her little baby brother,

Robert. She had poured the boiling water into the bath, and then undressed the baby, without remembering to pour in cold water to cool the bath.

Jenny put her elbow into the bath to double-check that the water was not too hot for Robert. As she put her elbow into the water, she realised that it was still boiling hot. Her elbow was scalded, however, she quickly pulled baby Bobby upwards and away from the bath. She gently laid the baby down in his cot again. He arm was very sore, as most burns are. Yet Jenny was thankful that the accident had happened to her, and not to the baby. Sometime, double-checking is a good way to avoid accidents.

Jesus talked about the accident on the farm, when a sheep fell into a hole on the Sabbath day. The Farmer pulled the poor beast out of the hole, even though it meant working on the Sabbath (Holy) Day. According to religious laws, Jewish people were not supposed to work on the sabbath. Jesus said that it was wise to do good on the Sabbath.

Prayer:

> Lord, our loving Heavenly Father,
> Help us all to avoid causing accidents.
> We pray for children who are in hospital,
> because of being knocked down on the roads.
> We pray that we may avoid accidents
> in the school, or in our homes. Make us wise.   Amen.

Hymn:

> At the name of Jesus. (C&P.1. 58), (JP. 13)

Teachers' Note: (1) Accidents may happen to anyone, at any time. (2) Accidents are often caused by our own thoughtlessness. (3) Accidents often may be avoided by double-checking. Accidents may happen. Reference. Matthew Chapter 12 verses 10, 11, 12. 13.

(a) Salt of the Earth

Week 12   Sayings of Jesus

(**Teacher:** A salt- cellar would be a good illustration to begin this assembly.)

Jesus said a strange thing to his Disciples. He said, "You are the salt of the earth."

I wonder if the Disciples understood what he meant. When we think of salt there may be two ideas in our minds.

First, Salt works even though it is a small thing. When Mother makes a meal, if it happens to be porridge at breakfast, she only puts a pinch of salt into the boiling porridge pot. If she is baking home-made bread, she only needs to put a pinch of salt among the dough, and the bread tastes right. If the farmer's wife is making butter in the milk churn, she only mixes into the butter, a tiny pinch of salt.

Did you know that salt was looked upon as valuable, in the days of the Roman Empire. Often the Roman soldiers would get paid their wage in salt. This is why wages are sometimes called, "Salaries" because the word "salary" comes from "salt." We have learnt that Salt works best in small quantities, but that it effects the whole meal. We also know that when it was scarce, it was it was considered to be valuable.

When Jesus said, "You are the Salt of the earth", he meant that even though Christians may only be a small group, they have a wide effect on the community. When there were no hospitals in Britain, it was the early church people who cared for sick people. Just as Mother Teresa, or the early missionary Nurses and Doctors opened hospitals in India, or Africa, for instance. The first hospitals were usually attached to church institutions.

When in the year 1665, the Black Plague swept across London, and thousands of people died in the epidemic, it was church people who visited the very sick people, and often buried the dead. Being the salt of the earth, means that just as salt flavours everything it touches, so Christians effect the whole community, even though it may only be a small Christian group.

During the great fire of London, the wooden houses, close together in the streets, caught fire. The fire, after a time, seemed to have destroyed the Black Plague germs. By their willingness to help the sick people, we learn that a small group of Christians are like salt in the soup. They affect every part.

Secondly, Salt may lose its taste. Salt is made in parts of the world, especially at the Dead Sea. The people allow the salty sea to flow over the rocky flat shore, until a shallow lake has been made. Then, when the tide goes out again, the hot sun dries up the water, and leaves a lake of dried salt behind. The native people sweep up the salt into heaps. It is put into sacks, and carried away to market to sell. Sometimes the salt would be lying out in the sun, for years at a time. The burning sun would shine on the salt every day, until after a long time, the salt would lose its saltiness.

Now tasteless salt is no use for anything. It would be no use to a cook or to a baker. Jesus said that salt which had lost its flavour was fit only to be thrown out and walked underfoot. Tasteless salt is useless salt.

The next time that you get the opportunity to see Leonardo da Vinci's famous painting of the "Last Supper" be sure to look at the twelve disciples eating at the Table, with Jesus." If you look more carefully at the picture, you will see that Judas Iscariot has accidentally knocked over the salt cellar. This is the artist's method of pointing out that Judas Iscariot has sacrificed (betrayed) Jesus. (Jews always sprinkled salt over the animal they were sacrificing to God).

Do not ever give up your values of faith, honesty, kindness, and willingness to do your best.

Prayer:

> Heavenly Father, help us to be the salt of the earth.
> May we not lose our faith in Jesus.
> May we work together, to help each other.
> We pray for poor and hungry people.
> We pray for any who are sick at this time. (name here).
> Through Jesus Christ our Lord.   Amen.

Hymn:

Our Father, who art in heaven. (C&P. 1. 51) (J.P. 192).

Teachers' Note: (1) Salt works in minute quantities. (2) Salt may lose it saltiness. Loss of faith is very sad. (3) Salt usually effects the whole of a meal. There is no telling just how much good a few Christians may do for their community. Reference Matthew Chapter 5, verse 13.

(b) Narcissus and Jesus

Week 12   Sayings of Jesus

Can you tell the difference between a Narcissus flower and a Daffodil flower? Which one has white petals, and which one has yellow petals? (Answer, Narsissus has white petals, and Daffodil has yellow petals). Which flower grows singly (alone) and which flower grows in groups? (Answer; the Narcissus grows alone, and the daffodil grows in groups).

Narcissus and the Well

The Greeks tell the story that Narcissus was a handsome young man, who lived in past times. He thought of himself as the most handsome person in the world. Narcissus was really in love with himself. He often looked down a well, and used it as a mirror, to admire himself. He was vain, and very conceited because of his own good looks.

One day, as he looked down the well, he saw a reflection of himself in the water. He was so beautiful, that he thought the reflection was that of a most beautiful young girl. He tried to reach the reflection in the well. He leaned over too far. He fell into the well, was drowned. He was never seen again.

The Greeks say that the Nymphs (beautiful fairy-like girls) came that night to take away his body for the funeral. However, all they could find was a single flower growing by the side of the well. This flower, growing alone, they named, "Narcissus."

Jesus at Jacob's Well

Here is a second story. Jesus was travelling towards Galilee, and he was passing through Samaria. He came to a town called Sy-char. Outside the town there was a well. It was known as "Jacob's Well." It was a very warm day, and Jesus sat down beside the well. He was tired after walking so far. There were no water taps in those days, only the water from the underground well was available. Jesus had no cup with him to drink from, nor had he a rope, nor a stone jar to bring up the water from the well.

The Disciples had gone into the town to buy food. As Jesus sat alone, a Samaritan woman came to draw water from the well. Now, the Samaritans and the Jews did not get on well together, and you will remember that Jesus was a Jew. Jews and Samaritans usually did not speak to each other. Jesus spoke to the woman, "Please, give me a drink," he said.

The woman replied, "How is it that you a Jew, are asking for a drink from me. I, who am a Samaritan." Jesus said to her, "If only you knew who was asking you for a drink, you would have asked from him, instead, and he would have given you living water. (Living water here means running or flowing water. The water from the well was still water.)

The woman said to Jesus, "Are you greater than our father Jacob, who gave us this well, and used it to provide water for himself, and for his family, and his cattle?" Jesus said, "He who drinks of the water from this well, will thirst again. However, he who drinks of the water that I shall give him, will never thirst. Instead, he will have in himself, a well of water, springing up into everlasting life." The woman answered again, "Sir, give me this water, so that I never will thirst, nor need to come back to this well again."

The woman again told Jesus that she was a Samaritan, and that she worshipped God on the mountain. (Jews taught that people should worship God in the city of Jerusalem). Jesus helped her understand that as long as we genuinely worship God, that is the important thing.

The conversation was drawing to a close. The woman said, that she knew that the Messiah (the Christ) was to come, and that when he came, that he would teach them the truth. Jesus looked at the Samaritan woman, and said, "I am he!"

What the living water in the story meant.

Jesus meant that his religion, the life of faith, would be like a bubbling spring of water inside the person who believes in him. Joy can be like a bubbling stream inside Christians. The main point is that to believe in Jesus, is to have a satisfying religion inside you.

Prayer:

> Gracious Father, we your children,
> thank you, for the satisfying gift of water.
> We remember that Jesus taught his friends,
> that to believe in Him,
> provides a satisfying joy in our hearts.
> We thank you for the water of life.   Amen.

Hymn:

> Have you heard the raindrops drumming on the roof-tops. (C&P.1. 2)

Teachers' Note: (1) The story of the woman at the well is an adult story, with symbolic words, meaning "salvation". Maybe, it is better to tell the Bible story, and to leave the children time to think about it, at their own age level. (2) The Narcissus story is only a fable. Narcissus loved himself. Jesus loved other people. (3) The Jesus story is a true encounter.

(c) The two Fears   *Week 12   Sayings of Jesus*

Paul was afraid of going up in an aircraft. He used to look up at the clouds, and think about the people sitting in aeroplanes. The very thought of going higher made his heart beat fast. When his parents decided to go to Paris on holiday, and to make the journey by plane, it made Paul most fearful, indeed. At night he used to dream about flying. He would wake up in terror.

Finally, the holiday date came round. The family packed their suit-cases, and they all boarded the taxi, which was to take them to the air-port. Paul began to cry. His Dad was very sympathetic. Dad told him that air-travel was the safest method of travelling. He also said that everyone feels a little nervous on their first flight.

Eventually they reached the air-port at Manchester. They presented their tickets and passports to the lady behind the airport counter. She took their baggage, put it on scales, and weighed it She stuck labels on each of the bags and cases, and passed them to the luggage Porter.

"This is it," thought Paul, as he stood with his family in the passenger queue. The Air-Hostess smiled at them. She called out the numbers of their seats, and showed them where to sit in the long aircraft. The Air-Hostess read aloud to everyone the rules of behaviour, should there ever be an emergency. She showed them that there were life-jackets under their seats. There were also oxygen masks in a little compartment over their heads.

Soon, the Pilot warmly welcomed them, speaking through a microphone. A bell rang, and all the cabin crew sat down on their seats. They put seat belts around their waists. The plane moved slowly at first, and then faster, until it lifted off the runway, and zoomed up into the sky. Paul was fascinated by how simple it all was. He even looked through the window, and gazed at the fields and roads far below. Paul thought to himself, how silly I was to be afraid. This is the loveliest experience of my whole life. I shall never be afraid of flying again!

At school, Hazel sat in the same class group as Paul. She was also afraid of going higher. Only, it was different from Paul's fear. She was eleven years old, and it was close to the end of the school term. She had to go higher to the Secondary School in August. She was terrified of moving up. She had attended the Primary School since she was five years old. For six years of her life, Hazel had felt safe. Now she had to leave her happy school. She had to attend a larger school, and mix with different older pupils. She really was terrified.

When they reached the last day at the Primary School, the Head-Teacher took the morning Assembly. He told them a story, they sang a hymn, and the Head-Teacher said to them, "For many of you this will be your last day at this school. We shall miss those who are leaving. We wish you well in the Secondary School."

He said, "Going up is always more difficult than going down. Going up is always a more hopeful way of living." Jesus said, "I will never leave you, nor forsake you." The Old Testament name that Christians often apply to Jesus is, "Immanuel." Now this name Immanuel, means, "God with us." So what have we to be afraid of, if God is with us?" Then the Teachers all looked at the children in the Assembly, and they repeated together, the prayer: "The Lord be with you."

The children answered: "And also with you." Amen.

Hazel realised that this prayer was for every pupil of eleven years of age, who was going up to the new school. Hazel thought to herself, "If the Lord Jesus is with me at the next school, then I need never be afraid." A great change came over Hazel. She was never again afraid of going up to the high School.

At the Secondary School, she met some old friends from her Primary School. She also made many new friends from other schools in the district. She felt that she had grown up all at once. Can you guess who was sitting beside her in her first form in the Secondary School? Yes! It was Paul.

He told her that he wanted to learn more mathematics, because, he wanted one day to join the air-crew of a passenger aircraft. Hazel told Paul that she would like to become a Teacher in a Secondary School, when she grew up. Both had conquered their fears of going higher.

Prayer:

> Heavenly Father, show us how to make progress.
> May we never be afraid of going onward in life.
> Lord bless, and encourage, all Primary School children,
> who are going to a higher school this year.
> Help them in their new forms.
> Grant to them your peace.   Amen.

Hymn:

> The ink is black. The page is white. (C&P.1. 67),
> or, One more step along the world I go. (C&P.47. 1), (JP. 188)

Teachers' Note: (1) Paul was really afraid of the unknown. (2) Hazel was also afraid of the unknown. (3) Both conquered their fears. We can go higher, when we realise that the Lord is always with us, wherever we may go. The Lord will never leave us. Immanuel Ref; Isaiah Chap. 7 verse 14, and Matthew Ch. 1 verse 23.